THRUSTING FORWARD

Editor and Production Coordinator: Charles A. Anezis
Designer: Peter Good
Printer: Eastern Press
Typographer: New England Typographic Service, Inc.

Printed in the United States with Inmont inks

THRUSTING FORWARD

A History of the Propeller

By George Rosen
with Charles A. Anezis

Published by   Hamilton Standard
Division of United Technologies Corporation

British Aerospace Dynamics Group
Hatfield-Lostock Division

Fifty years ago, on June 1, 1934 to be exact, our companies began a formal association that continues to this day. At the time it involved the manufacture of controllable pitch propellers. In the intervening years our relationship has grown into other programs and other products. We enthusiastically look forward to working together in the years ahead.

To commemorate our 50th anniversary, we are greatly pleased to publish *Thrusting Forward*. This book is an informal history of the aircraft propeller, the product on which our companies were founded. It also is a tribute to the men and women who have contributed in large and small measure to the propeller's proud past and its promising future.

We sincerely hope you enjoy reading this book as much as we have enjoyed publishing it.

John Lovkay

President
Hamilton Standard
Division of United Technologies
Corporation

Bernard J. Rosser

Managing Director
Hatfield-Lostock Division
British Aerospace Dynamics Group

	Page
Contents	

About the Author

George Rosen, chief of propeller research and development at Hamilton Standard before he retired in 1977, has devoted his entire professional career to the advancement of the aircraft propeller. Much of the source material for this book came from historical information he has compiled over the years for a definitive history of the propeller he plans to publish.

Mr. Rosen became Hamilton Standard's first propeller aerodynamicist in 1937, the year he graduated from the Massachusetts Institute of Technology. He held a succession of senior engineering positions during his 40 years with the company. An associate fellow of the American Institute of Aeronautics and Astronautics, he received the AIAA's prestigious Goddard Award in 1975 in recognition of his major contributions in the development of the turbine propeller. Mr. Rosen holds a number of patents, including one for the variable camber propeller for which he was awarded United Technologies' George Mead Medal in 1961 for outstanding individual achievement.

Acknowledgments

This book could only have been published with the efforts of many individuals and organizations. We acknowledge with the deepest gratitude the invaluable advice and assistance of Desmond Thurgood, chief mechanical engineer at the Hatfield-Lostock Division of the British Aerospace Dynamics Group.

Special thanks for their guidance also are extended to Robert B. Meyer, former curator of propulsion of the Smithsonian Institution's Air and Space Museum, and Harvey Lippincott, archivist of United Technologies Corporation.

For their permission to use many of the photographs published in this book we want to give special credit to the British Science Museum, Royal Air Force Museum, the Royal Aeronautical Society, the Smithsonian Air and Space Museum, the U.S. Air Force Museum and the publications *After the Battle* and *Flight.*

Introduction

The aircraft propeller—with the clean, graceful lines of its blades and smooth, sculpted roundness of its spinner —looks like a simple mechanism. The simplicity of its appearance, however, is deceiving for the propeller embodies the highest sophistication in aerodynamics, mechanical engineering and structural design.

Essentially a wing, the rotating propeller converts its "lift" into thrust. The propeller's rotation and the angle at which the blades strike the air control aircraft speed in all phases of flight while the engine's speed remains constant and the aircraft's speed and altitude vary. Varying, too, across the blade from hub to tip are the direction and velocity of the air flowing through the propeller.

The environment in which a propeller operates can be severe. It must survive loose stones, rain, snow, hail, sea spray, and sand storms, lightning strikes, even unfortunate birds that get into its path. Air temperatures during a flight can range anywhere from −65 to +165 degrees Fahrenheit (−55 to +75 degrees Celsius).

Much greater in severity are the continuing stresses experienced by the propeller. Its blades constantly bend, flex, twist and vibrate, and the loads and forces are transmitted to the engine and airframe. Both steady and dynamic, these stresses are tremendous.

The centrifugal forces of today's commuter propeller, for example, exerts a pull of 25 tons on the blades and their retention in the hub. On the other hand, the propeller's thrust produces a bending force of more than half a ton on each blade. Typically, the combined rotational and forward speeds result in propeller tip speeds approaching Mach 0.8. Any change, gradual or sudden, in aircraft speed and maneuvers alters the angle at which air flows into the propeller disc, causing an imbalance in the dynamic forces and magnifying them.

Structurally, the blades must be thick and strong enough to handle these stresses and loads. Conversely, they must be thin enough for the best thrust efficiency and light enough to minimize the propeller's weight. And the propeller must be carefully integrated with engine and airframe so that its aerodynamic loads and mechanical stresses are transmitted without any dynamic problems.

These are only some of the often conflicting considerations that go into the propeller's design and manufacture. They give the lay person some appreciation of the complexity of the propeller and the importance of its aeronautical role.

This general history briefly relates how the knowledge of the propeller's aerodynamic and structural characteristics were gained and applied, from ancestral beginnings to the present day. Admittedly, this story is told from the perspective and experience of Hamilton Standard and the Dynamics Group. A conscientious attempt, nevertheless, has been made to acknowledge the many other companies and individuals who also have contributed so significantly to the development and success of the aircraft propeller.

1

THE ANCESTORS:REAL AND IMAGINED

*The propeller, descended from two, possibly
three ideas, is first used to move boats. To aviation's earliest
pioneers, it poses a mechanical mystery.*

The genealogy of the aircraft propeller can be traced back to two, possibly three, sources of inspiration. One is the helical screw concept which Archimedes, the Greek mathematician who lived in the Third Century B.C., invented to transport water uphill. Leonardo da Vinci, that epitome of Renaissance man, appears to have been the first European to adapt the helical idea to the airscrew. His concept of a helical screw helicopter (c. 1490), some historians claim, is the ancestor of both the air propeller and the helicopter rotor.

In searching to prove one of his theories, da Vinci also discovered that, by rapidly twirling a wide, thin ruler, he could feel a strong pull on his arm in the direction of the rotational axis. Two centuries later pioneering aerodynamicists were seeking to produce this kind of thrust by reversing the windmill's normal function of extracting energy from the wind. Instead, they wanted to use energy to rotate the sails, push air toward the rear, and thus move forward whatever vehicle it was attached to.

The propeller could be a descendant of the Chinese flying top, invented in some prehistoric age. The toy flew vertically when its spindle, with feathers inserted at right angles, was rotated rapidly. The helicopter toys, which Launoy and Bienvenu in France and Sir George Cayley in England used in their flight experiments, could have been variations of the Chinese toy. There is some dispute over any connection between the two, however, based on the argument that early Chinese writings were unknown to the Western World until recently. Yet others claim that Marco Polo or other European merchant explorers could have brought the idea back from China.

It is undisputed, however, that the idea of a propulsive airscrew was revived in Europe by J. P. Paucton, the French mathematician. In his treatise "Theorie de la vis d'Archimede" published in 1768, he described a flying machine, the Pterophore, fitted with two airscrews, one for propulsion and the other for sustaining flight.

Many early experimenters in marine and air propulsion used the helical screw concept during the late 1700s and early 1800s. It wasn't long, however, before they discovered that more propulsive power could be mustered by partly straightening the helical blades' surfaces.

Because water is a denser medium than air, it's not surprising that the first practical application of the propulsive screw was in ships. As near as can be determined, the first use of a marine propeller occurred in 1776 during the American Revolution. Inventor David Bushnell's submarine Turtle was propelled by a crude, hand-cranked screw when it made an abortive attempt to sink a British man-of-war in New York Harbor. The prototype of future generations of marine screws was invented by John Ericcson, a Swedish engineer studying in London in 1835. The propeller that won him a British Admiralty prize had six blades, each set at an appropriate angle by spokes held in a hub.

山海經

奇肱國其人一臂三目有陰有陽能作
飛車從風遠行在一臂國北

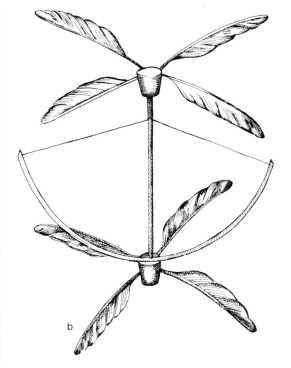

b

d

c

a—Chinese flying chariot (c. 200 B.C.) used propeller-like wheels.

b—Airscrew-type helicopter toy by Sir George Cayley may have descended from Chinese flying top.

c—Leonardo da Vinci's spring-driven helicopter is an ancestor of the air propeller and helicopter rotor.

d—Helical marine propeller invented by Benjamin D. Beecher was mounted on the bow of his experimental steamboat. Patent drawing shows counter-rotating, coaxial propeller whose height could be adjusted according to water's depth.

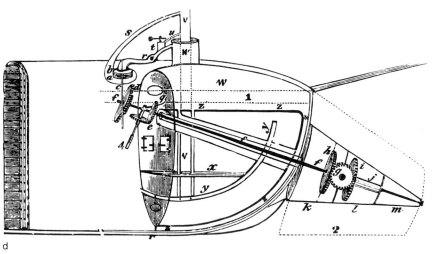

d

a

a—Ascent of de Rozier and Laurent in a
Montgolfier balloon on November 21, 1783
heralded man's first aerial voyage.

b—The "le Comet d'Artois" balloon
flown by Frenchmen Alban and Vallet in 1785
had hand-cranked propeller forward
with side-mounted flapping oars.

b

While air-propeller inventors were experimenting with helical designs, considerable work in propellers with straight blades was going on in Europe, particularly in France. The first to successfully use such an air propeller for horizontal propulsion was Vallet, a chemical manufacturer. On July 2, 1784 he tested a hand-driven device on a boat on the Seine River. A contemporary reported that the boat with the "wheel composed of blades . . . which provide motion" sailed faster than and carried twice as many passengers as its oar-propelled competitor.

Ballooning was gaining in popularity at this time, less than a year after Jean-Francois Pilatre de Rozier and Francois Laurent, the marquis d'Arlandes, made man's first aerial voyage (November 21, 1783) in a Montgolfier balloon. Attempts to convert these fickle, free-flying (and dangerous) machines into steerable, effectively propelled dirigibles met with numerous frustrations. Some of the more fanciful solutions included ship sails, bird traction, oars, paddle wheels and even a gas bag shaped in a huge helical screw that was to spin through the air. Propellers also were thought of, but they were as yet impractical. The first to seriously attempt to use an airborne propeller was the famous French balloonist Jean-Pierre Francois Blanchard. Accompanied by Professor John Sheldon, an Englishman who turned the hand propeller which "acted on the air as a screw to advance the calm," Blanchard made a balloon ascent on October 16, 1784 from the Military Academy in Chelsea, London. He called the device "moulinet," or little windmill, an acknowledgment of the source of his idea. It proved ineffective.

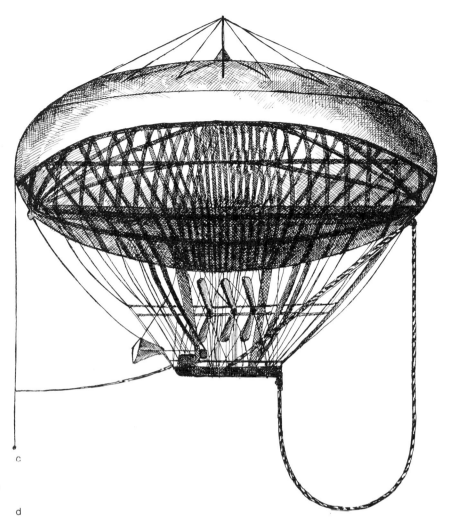

c

d

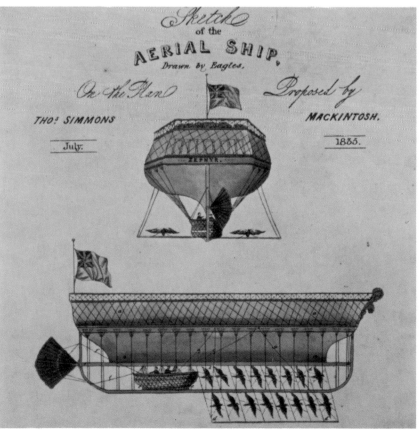

c—Airship conceived by J. B. M. Meusnier in 1785 was driven by three, 40-foot propellers and manually operated by windlasses.

d—Fancies of flight, this one using bird power for propulsion, persisted into the mid-1800s.

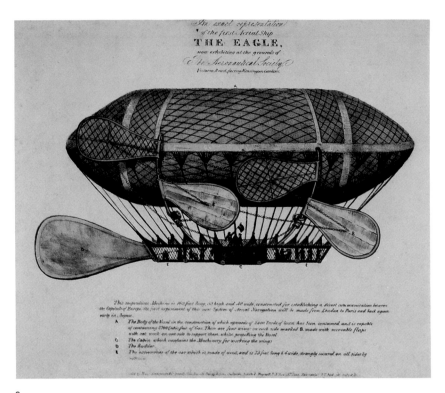

a

On January 7 the following year, this time with the American Dr. John Jeffries as a passenger, he made the first aerial crossing of the English Channel. Part of the way across, the gas bag's hydrogen began leaking excessively. The balloonists, losing altitude fast, managed to reach the French coast, but not before they jettisoned the useless propeller and other expendable items, including the men's outergarments and, as one historian noted, their "breeches", too.

At the very birth of the age of flight we see the propeller evolving from such basic concepts as Archimedes' helical screw and the windmill. It was being increasingly recognized as a potentially effective means of aerial propulsion. If man was to achieve sustained, controlled flight, however, he would have to master, among other things, the mysteries of the propeller and the mechanical power to turn it. These monumental tasks remained for aviation's visionaries to tackle in the 19th century.

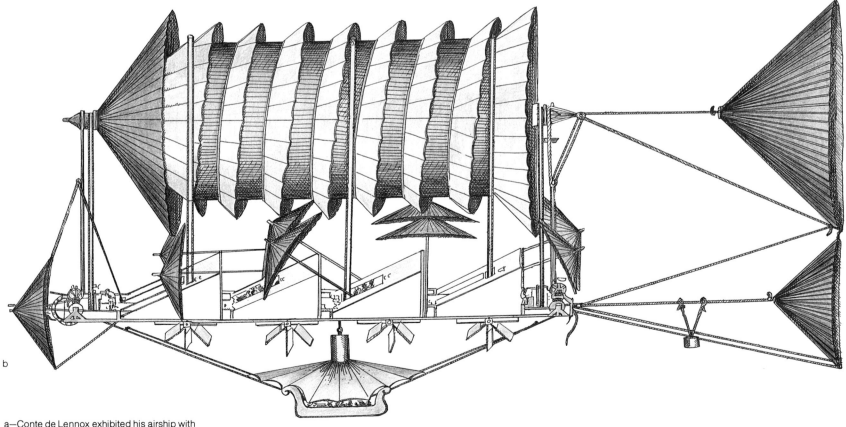

b

a—Conte de Lennox exhibited his airship with huge paddles in London in 1835.

b—Among the most fanciful was this airship, literally a giant spinning helical screw proposed by Pierre Ferrand in 1835.

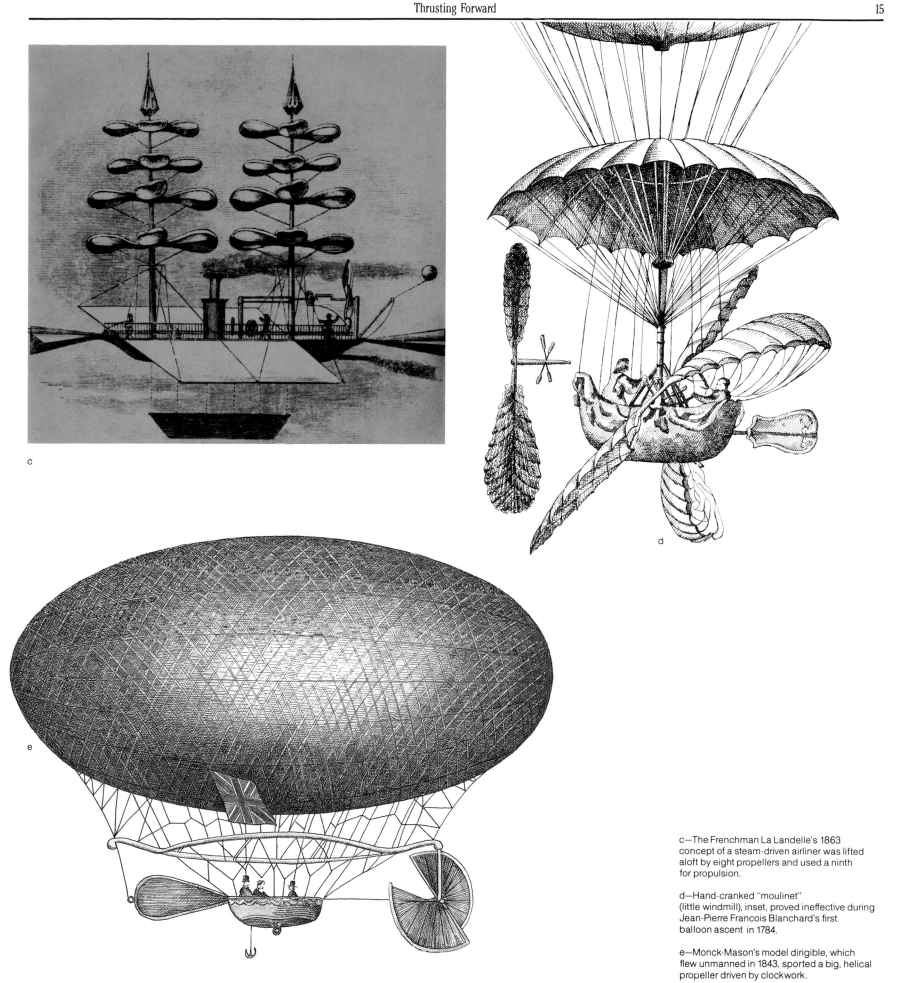

c—The Frenchman La Landelle's 1863 concept of a steam-driven airliner was lifted aloft by eight propellers and used a ninth for propulsion.

d—Hand-cranked "moulinet" (little windmill), inset, proved ineffective during Jean-Pierre Francois Blanchard's first balloon ascent in 1784.

e—Monck-Mason's model dirigible, which flew unmanned in 1843, sported a big, helical propeller driven by clockwork.

2

THE ERA OF EXPERIMENTATION

Experimenters begin to understand and tentatively use the propeller on dirigibles and aircraft models. They, however, still don't fully appreciate its aerodynamic importance to the success of flight.

Throughout the 19th century, aviation's early pioneers explored the concepts of flight and tried to combine them into a viable aerial ship. In their attempts to transform the spherical, free-flying balloons into navigable cigar-shaped airships, balloonists repeatedly tried sails, propellers and paddle wheels—all with very limited results.

Other experimenters, convinced that manned flight should have wings, struggled to establish the basic principles in the new scientific fields of aerodynamics and flight stability and control as well as propulsion. Some, taking their cue from the familiar windmill, worked with blades; others returned to the Archimedean screw.

Among the screw propeller's believers were two nephews of Napoleon Bonaparte who, from 1823 to 1828, conducted what many believe to be the first broad scientific investigation of propellers. Napoleon-Louis and his 15-year-old brother, the future Napoleon III, first measured thrust effectiveness by recording the speeds of a propeller-driven car model moving along a tight wire. They then ran full-scale tests by mounting helical screw propellers on a tethered hot-air balloon. These propellers were powered by using a falling weight to unwind a rope on a spool.

First to successfully apply mechanical power to a man-carrying airship was Henri Giffard, the famous French railway engineer. He mounted a small, 3 horsepower steam engine driving a three-blade propeller, 11 feet in diameter, at 110 revolutions per minute on a gondola platform under an elliptical gas bag. Grandly attired in top hat and frock coat, Giffard on September 24, 1852 flew from the Hippodrome in Paris to Elancourt 17 miles away at about five miles an hour. Significant though this accomplishment was, Giffard couldn't make the complete circuit. That required a more efficient, lighter weight engine.

Controlled mechanical flight finally came on August 9, 1884. Two French Army captains, Charles Renard and A. C. Krebs, flew the airship La France on a closed circuit from Chalais-Meudon to Villacoublay and back in 23 minutes. La France, powered by a 9 horsepower electric motor driving a two-blade airscrew 23 feet in diameter, reached a speed of 14½ miles per hour and was able to return to the starting point on most of its six flights. The flight marked the birth of the dirigible, a steerable lighter-than-air ship with adequate propulsion.

Meanwhile, in their search for effective winged flight, experimenters delved into the very nature of air itself. Through trial and error, they studied the interacting forces and flows produced by a wing moving through air. Chief among these researchers was Sir George Cayley, a British theorist acclaimed widely as the father of aerodynamics. Although his work never materialized into powered winged flight, he established the sound aerodynamic principles that were essential to the success of others.

Cayley's interest in aerodynamics and manned flight spanned more than 50 years—from 1792 to his death in 1857. Early in his career he conceived an aircraft design that was the

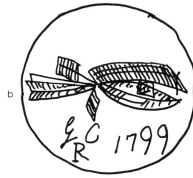

a

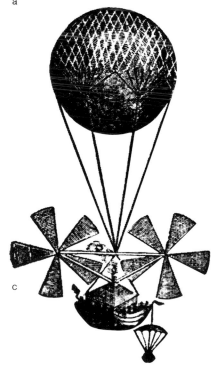

c

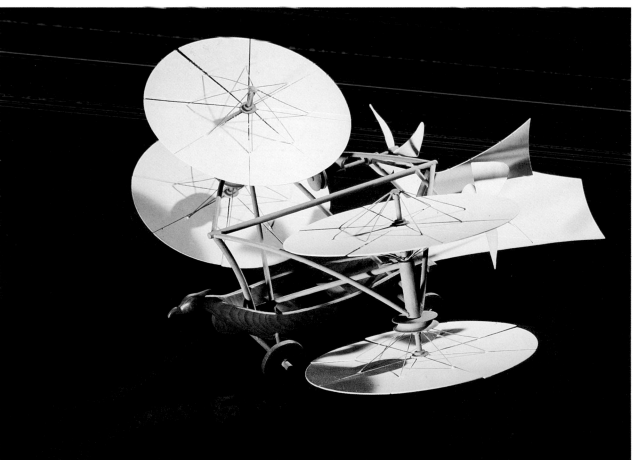

d

a—Performance of a helical screw propeller was measured by Napoleon brothers on this tethered balloon in Italy during 1828.

b—Sir George Cayley's prophetic design of an aircraft (1799) featured cambered wings, pilot's cockpit, horizontal and vertical tail section. Later versions replaced paddles with a propeller.

c—Dirigible conceived by Cayley (1837) offered alternative propulsion—flapping wings or propellers—driven by steam engine.

d—Cayley's convertiplane (1843) presaged today's compound helicopter, part aircraft and part helicopter.

a

first in history to include cambered wings, a nacelle-shaped fuselage and a tail combining rudder and elevator. Interestingly enough, his drawing initially showed two paddles for propulsion, but by 1804, after more investigation, he became a steadfast proponent of the propeller.

Testing his theories with model and full-scale gliders, Cayley hypothesized some of the aerodynamic principles needed to design a man-carrying aircraft. The problem, as he saw it, was to make a surface that could "support a given weight by the application of sufficient power to overcome the resistance of air." That sufficient power—a lightweight, self contained power plant—was a half century away, waiting for the automobile to be fitted first with a compact, internal combustion engine that burned gasoline or some other liquid fuel.

Until then aircraft designers were forced to power their aircraft by crude steam engines. Influenced by Cayley's research, two of his countrymen, William Henson and John Stringfellow, tested models of their modern-looking monoplanes driven by twin pusher propellers, but their work was stymied by steam power's weight and inefficiencies. Felix du Temple constructed the first aircraft model to make an unassisted takeoff in 1857. The 1½ pound monoplane was driven by a clockwork-cranked tractor propeller and later was powered by steam. Its ability to take off was attributed to large-span cantilevered wings set at a high angle of attack, a streamlined hull and the high thrust produced by a 12-blade propeller.

In 1875 in London's Crystal Palace, Thomas Moy's large-scale model Aerial Streamer reached 33 miles an hour and lifted about six inches off the board track while tethered but that was all. Its twin, 12-foot diameter propellers had six blades each. The twist of each blade's eight slats could be adjusted to produce maximum thrust under certain conditions, an early recognition of the need for changing the blade pitch.

Research done by Alphonse Penaud blazed the aeronautical trail for many designers who followed him for many years. His design of an amphibious aircraft, patented in 1876, anticipated many of the elements of successful flight—stressed skin wing, enclosed cockpit, retractable landing gear, single control column and controllable-pitch propellers.

The brilliant young Frenchman also devised propellers driven by twisted rubber-band motors to power the remarkably light and stable model planes he used to test his extensive research in flight aerodynamics. He established the design criteria for lateral and longitudinal stability and compensated for the propeller's torque by slightly twisting one side of a wing or adding a light weight to the other side. He considered the three principal problems of aerial flight to be drag, strength of materials and lightweight power plants.

In Great Britain, Horatio Phillips also made significant contributions to the aerodynamics of lift and propulsion. Following two decades of studies and experiments, he conceived a

a—Although W. S. Henson's model Aerial Steam Carriage never flew, its modern concept influenced inventors who followed him.

b—Model triplane with two pusher propellers and a 28-square-foot wing area was exhibited by John Stringfellow in 1868.

c—Sketches show Alphonse Penaud's "paddle-wheel" aircraft models which used rubber-band motors to rotate wings in opposite directions, and producing both lift and forward propulsion.

d—The first U. S. propeller-driven flight was made over Hartford, Connecticut, on June 12, 1878 by a flying machine designed by Professor Charles F. Ritchel. The small, hydrogen-filled gas bag had two manually operated propellers. The one in front, steered by foot pedals, propelled the machine and also provided directional control. The other, mounted horizontally under the pilot's seat, produced thrust for ascents and altitude control during flight.

e—Henri Giffard was the first to fly an airship (1852) with mechanical power—a 3 horsepower steam engine driving a propeller 11 feet in diameter.

f—Modern-looking aircraft model of Victor Tatin used propellers with cambered blades and was driven by compressed-air motors when it made a tethered flight in 1879.

g—Laminated wood propeller Horatio Phillips built for his experimental steam-driven aircraft in 1893 was stiffened by ribs at the blade's widest chord.

h—Airship conceived by Henri Dupuy de Lome in 1872 was fitted with two-bladed propeller 30 feet in diameter manually cranked by an eight-man crew.

b

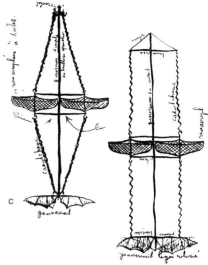

c

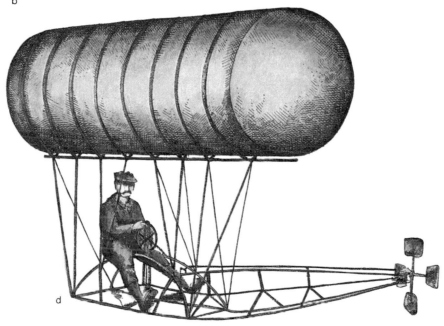

d

e

f

g

h

curved aerofoil, the Phillips Entry, that he patented in 1884 and refined in 1891. Aerodynamically more advanced than the works of Cayley and Henson, his aerofoil considerably improved a wing's lift-drag ratios by combining a cambered surface with a uniquely shaped leading edge.

As the end of the 19th century approached, the pace of attempts at full-scale powered flights quickened as aircraft builders were encouraged by advanced steam engine designs and the advent of the lighter, more efficient gasoline motor. Some came close to succeeding.

One of these was Aleksandr Mozhaysky who designed and built a steam-driven monoplane in Russia in 1884. Launched down the ramp of a ski jump, it managed to get airborne for a few seconds before hitting the ground. Between 1890 and 1897 the French self-made engineer, Clement Ader, tried to fly his bat-like steam propelled Eole monoplane several times, but it managed to leave the ground only once when it crashed. His flexible, feather-shaped blades permitted the adjustment of blade twist and changes in camber under different aerodynamic load conditions, much like the feathers of a bird, but the machines possessed only marginal propulsive power, and their control in flight was inadequate.

Perhaps the most expensive project of this period was carried out by Sir Hiram Maxim, an American expatriate and inventor of the machine gun. His many years of experiments (he tested at least 30 different propellers alone) culminated in the construction in 1890 of a huge, four-ton biplane which he tested on the rails of a straight track. Two 180 hp steam engines each drove propellers 17 feet, 10 inches in diameter and weighing 135 pounds.

The two-blade propellers, inversely tapered and squared at the tips 5½ feet wide, were made of overlapping strips of American pine, planed smooth and covered with glued canvas and stayed to the propeller shafts by steel wire to handle the high thrust loads. Under full power, these giant propellers each developed 1,100 pounds of thrust at speeds of 425 revolutions per minute. Maxim's project ended in calamity when, on one of its trial runs, the machine jumped the track and suffered extensive damage.

Few men pursued aeronautics as painstakingly and scientifically as the ill-fated Samuel P. Langley, the distinguished American inventor and mathematician. On a test flight on August 9, 1903, his quarter-scale model flew a distance of 1,000 feet in 27 seconds to become the first heavier-than-air model aircraft powered by a gasoline engine.

On December 8, from a floating dock on the Potomac River, Langley attempted to launch his full-scale, government-funded Aerodrome for a second time. The machine and its pilot again fell into the river when the catapult's force damaged the fragile airframe. Langley's only reward for his 20 years of aeronautical research was public criticism and ridicule, and the threat of a Congressional investigation for wasting public money.

Just nine days after Langley's abortive attempt to make the first controlled, sustained flight, Orville Wright rose from the sands of Kitty Hawk on man's first successful aircraft flight.

a

b

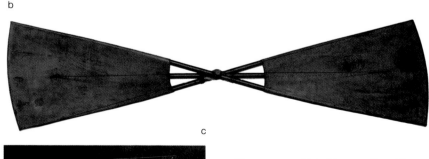

c

a—Steam-powered Eole flying machine with feather-like propeller was designed by Clement Ader in France.

b—Propeller designed by Samuel P. Langley for his Aerodrome tandem monoplane.

c—Looking like a Venetian blind, Phillips' multiplane tested his curved aerofoils which had a span of 19 feet. A small steam engine drove the tractor propeller.

d

d—Alberto Santos-Dumont's half-hour roundtrip (circling the Eiffel Tower midway) in his propeller-driven dirigible on October 19, 1901 finally won the public's confidence in airships.

e—Catapulted from a houseboat on the Potomac River, Langley's Aerodrome made two unsuccessful attempts to fly in 1903. Two propellers installed between the wings were powered by a radial, gasoline engine.

f—Maxim's huge demonstration flying machine was powered by a steam engine driving two wooden propellers each 18 feet in diameter.

f   e

3

THE WRIGHTS' MAGNIFICENT OBSESSION

*Before their historical flight, the Wright brothers studied and tested the aerodynamics
of flight step by step. "Nothing about the propeller and the medium in which
it acts, stands still for a moment," they found.*

Years after he made history's first controlled, powered flight on December 17, 1903, Orville Wright recalled that, while their preparatory work led his brother Wilbur and him to conclude that a propeller simply is a whirling wing, arriving at the calculations they needed to design their aircraft's propellers was another matter.

"Nothing about the propeller or the medium in which it acts, stands still for a moment," he wrote. "The thrust depends upon the speed and the angle at which the blade strikes the air; the angle at which the blade strikes the air depends upon the speed at which the propeller is turning, the speed at which the machine is traveling forward, and the speed at which the air is traveling backward.

"The slip of the air backward depends upon the thrust exerted by the propeller and the amount of air acted upon. When any of these change, it changes all the rest as they are all interdependent upon one another. But these are only a few of the many factors that must be considered and determined in calculating and designing propellers. Our minds became so obsessed with it that we could do little other work."

Perhaps the single, overriding characteristic of the Wrights' genius was the realization that all aspects of winged flight were interdependent—aerodynamics, structures, control and propulsion. Their remarkable research and experiments between 1900 and 1903 sought to solve three basic problems: constructing wings capable of sustaining flight; generating and

applying sufficient power to drive the machine through the air; balancing and steering the machine once it became airborne.

The brothers felt some progress had been made in wing and propulsion design but looked upon controlling the flying machine as the biggest problem they had to overcome. And it was their effective control of their machine's pitch, roll and yaw that ultimately led to their success where others had failed.

In fact, it was their study of birds and of the glider experiments of the German Otto Lilienthal, who was primarily concerned with the stability and control of his machines, that inspired the Wrights—printers turned bicycle builders—to seriously take up aviation. Their basic textbook was *Progress in Flying Machines* by Octave Chanute, the French born, American educated engineer and a glider pioneer who became a close friend of the brothers and frequently corresponded with them.

Orville and Wilbur Wright conducted their studies and experiments methodically, step by step. Unlike many of their predecessors and contemporaries, they first set out to learn how to fly as Lilienthal had advocated before them. They began with kites in 1899, progressed to tethered gliders, then gliders in free flight. Only when they had painstakingly tested their theories did the Wrights prepare to apply them to practical design.

Since they had little information to guide them in understanding the fundamental principles of blade shape and motion, the Wrights found the propeller to be one of their most

a

a

b

a—Orville and Wilbur Wright flew kites, then gliders to verify their flight stability and control theories.

b—Orville Wright made history's first controlled, powered flight at Kitty Hawk, North Carolina, on December 17, 1903.

challenging problems. Research scientists in a true sense despite their lack of formal education, they learned from their investigations that large propeller diameters would produce high thrust for a given power input. They calculated the best rotational speed for such a propeller. They also found that the higher torque produced by large, slow turning propellers adversely affected a flying machine's control and stability.

For their design conditions of 24 miles an hour in flight, they chose two propellers, each 8½ feet in diameter and absorbing half the output of the four cylinder, 12 horsepower gasoline engine they built with the help of their assistant Charles Taylor. Designed to operate at 350 revolutions per minute, the propellers were installed behind the wings of the biplane to minimize airflow disturbance over the wings. To gain thrust efficiency by reducing the blades' rotational speed, the Wright brothers used a chain and sprocket transmission and crossed one of the chains to rotate the propellers in opposite directions. The ingenious yet simple arrangement of counterbalancing the torque of the revolving propellers eliminated one of the major control problems that had plagued other experimenters.

Contributing significantly to the Wrights' success was their decision to design and build large diameter, slow-turning propellers—an approach opposite to the small diameter, high speed and directly connected propellers that powered most aircraft of the period. Their propeller's thrust efficiency of 66% may seem puny compared to today's 90% levels, but it was much higher than any produced by propellers at the time.

With their characteristic thoroughness, Orville and Wilbur Wright also developed new structural design and fabrication methods. Calculating the severe structural loads the blades would undergo, they chose sturdy, kiln-dried spruce for its high strength-to-weight ratio. In shaping the blades, they roughed out the blocks of three laminates with hatchets and shaved the blades precisely to their calculations with drawknives. Lightweight canvas duck glued to the blade tips prevented the thin blades from splitting and provided some degree of protection against erosion.

Late in 1906 Alberto Santos-Dumont, a wealthy Brazilian living in Paris and an aviation pioneer, became the first European to fly a controlled machine as he coaxed his canard (tail first) biplane off the ground. His longest of six flights covered approximately 720 feet in 21 seconds. Wilbur Wright's series of demonstrations in France in 1908 emphasized to Europeans the importance of flight control and the technical methods the Wrights used to construct their propellers, engines and biplanes.

The foundations of a disciplined approach to propeller design evolved quickly. Out of the refinements advanced by experimental work conducted in England, France, Germany, Italy and Russia came the first true criteria that engineers could use to design propellers with better performance and structural reliability.

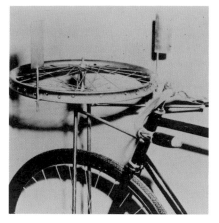

a—Before wind tunnel tests, the Wright brothers rode a specially rigged bicycle to check the validity of Otto Lilienthal's aerofoil data.

b—Thousands witnessed the Wright Brothers demonstration flights after their success, first in the U.S., later in Europe.

c—Crossing one transmission chain made the Wright Flyer pusher propellers rotate in opposite directions. This counterbalanced propeller torque and solved a flight control problem that had plagued aviation pioneers.

a

b

c

d

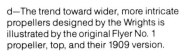

d—The trend toward wider, more intricate propellers designed by the Wrights is illustrated by the original Flyer No. 1 propeller, top, and their 1909 version.

e—Propeller and rib department of the Wrights' airplane factory in Dayton, Ohio (c. 1911).

f—Variety of propellers and blades designed and fabricated in Europe in the 1908–1910 period.

g—Early experimental blades of Hugo Junkers and Hans Reissner in Germany (c. 1909).

o

f

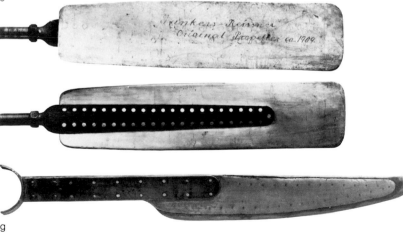

g

f

f

a—Variety of propellers and blades designed and fabricated in Europe in the 1908–1910 period.

b—Requa Gibson Company, the first U.S. propeller manufacturer, ran this advertisement in a 1910 issue of *Aircraft* magazine.

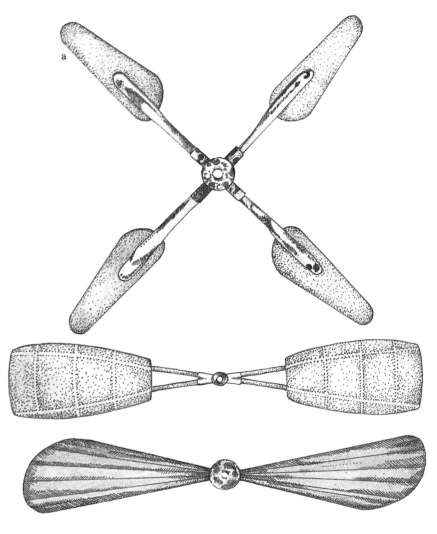

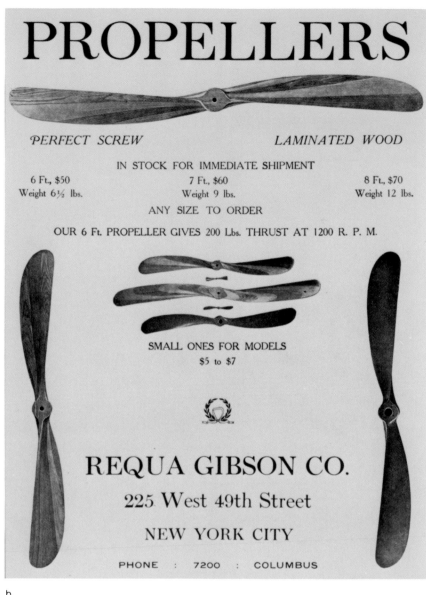

b

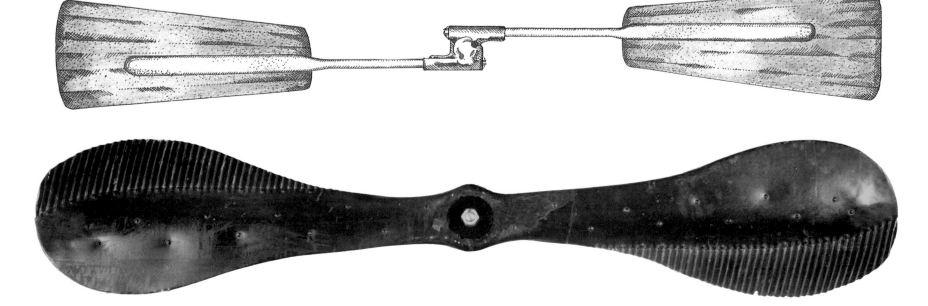

c—Driven also by a pusher propeller was Henri Farman's 1909 biplane which introduced "open" wings and tail, a forward elevator, four-wheel undercarriage with skids and ailerons at both ends of each wing.

d—First viable European aircraft was Gabriel Voisin's biplane which had a forward elevator, rudder inside a box-kite tail unit and a pusher propeller (1907).

They resulted in the production of the first generation of well engineered propellers. One of them was the Integrale, engineered by the Frenchman Lucien Chauviere, the world's first propeller manufacturer whose products became the standard of excellence in the nascent aviation industry. By 1910 the number of propeller producers multiplied through Europe and across the Atlantic Ocean. In France alone, Chauviere was being challenged by 18 companies, Motet, Ratier, Ratmanoff and Voisin being among the more notable.

While the majority of the pioneers were still striving to perfect wooden propellers, a few visionaries were experimenting with metal propellers and variable-pitch blades. In his search for a suitable propeller for his aircraft, the young English engineer Geoffrey deHavilland tested propellers whose aluminium blades could be adjusted to change their angle. At the same time, the German collaborators Hugo Junkers and Hans Reissner, probing the entire frontier of aircraft design, also experimented with lightweight metal propellers.

Like the companies deHavilland and Junkers founded, the Wrights and Glenn Curtiss in America designed and fabricated their own propellers as well as airframes and engines. The first to specialize in propeller production in the U.S. was the Requa Gibson Company founded in 1909. It first borrowed the Chauviere design, but out of Hugh C. Gibson's research evolved propellers with distinctive designs of their own.

Expanding on the work done by the Wright brothers, the Canadian engineer Wallace R. Turnbull tested and confirmed through tests the higher thrust efficiencies of large, slow-speed propellers compared to those of the smaller, high-speed versions. More importantly, from experiments conducted between 1908 and 1910, he confirmed the universal law of aerodynamics: the efficiency of any aerodynamic device rises as the amount of air it acts upon increases and the velocity of that air decreases.

It was during this period that F. W. Lanchester, the British automotive engineer, came out with his vortex, or circulation, theory of wing aerodynamics. His work, which formed the foundation of flight as we know it today, however, was so advanced that it wasn't until near the end of World War I that the German mathematician Ludwig Prandtl put the vortex theory to practical use. The Lanchester-Prandtl theory, first applied to wing analysis, was extended to propellers in the mid-1920s. It helped designers to better understand the aerodynamic behavior of propellers, although its application to a practical computational method was not perfected until many years later.

On July 25, 1909 Louis Bleriot, one of Europe's best pilots, flew his XI monoplane driven by a Chauviere Integrale propeller from Calais to Dover in 37 minutes. His achievement electrified the public's imagination and touched off countless air meets and aerial circuses that thrilled thousands of Europeans and Americans during aviation's adolescent years that ended with the beginning of World War I.

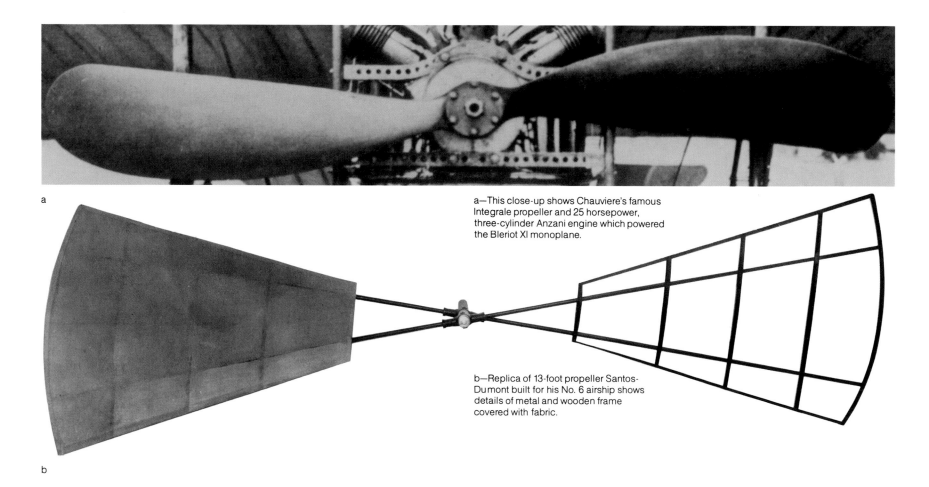

a—This close-up shows Chauviere's famous Integrale propeller and 25 horsepower, three-cylinder Anzani engine which powered the Bleriot XI monoplane.

b—Replica of 13-foot propeller Santos-Dumont built for his No. 6 airship shows details of metal and wooden frame covered with fabric.

c

c—On his English Channel crossing, French pilot Louis Bleriot flew 23½ miles in 37 minutes on July 25, 1909 in the XI which featured wing-warping for lateral control and a tail with a rudder and two elevators.

d—First commercial aircraft sale in the U.S. was the Curtiss "Golden Flier" shown taking off from a frozen lake. The Aeronautical Society bought it in 1909 to stage exhibition flights.

d

4

WORLD WAR I: BAPTISM OF FIRE

*The standardization of the design
and manufacture of wooden propellers emerges. Aircraft engines
change from steam power to internal combustion.*

The four years of World War I's duration brought advances in aircraft, engine and propeller performance that otherwise would have taken decades to make. Soon after the outbreak of the war, aircraft were being used for battlefield observation and reconnaissance because they were more maneuverable than dirigibles and balloons. Few among the military on both sides, however, thought about arming them or imagined that the aircraft was about to revolutionize warfare itself.

This was not surprising, considering the frailty of the airframes and the less than efficient and dependable engines that powered them. The best of the 1914 vintage aircraft could climb to about 3,000 feet and fly 200 miles at 70 miles an hour. The demands of combat, however, accelerated technical and production developments. Out of this impetus grew fleets of different warplanes for specific missions—scouts, armed reconnaissance aircraft, fighters and bombers. By the war's end single-seat fighters powered by 200 horsepower engines were battling at 15,000-foot altitudes, and bombers were penetrating deep in enemy territory at night as well as day.

The air war became a seesaw with the better aircraft on one side quickly being outperformed by the enemy's newer machine. One example indirectly involved the propeller. In April 1915 the famous French ace Roland Garros shot down a German aircraft by firing through the propeller of his single-seat craft. The propeller, an Integrale, was protected from the fighter's own machine-gun fire by metal deflector plates.

Shortly thereafter Garros was downed by ground fire and captured, along with his Morane-Saulnier aircraft. The Germans examined the metal deflector propeller and went one better by developing a machine gun synchronized to fire between the whirling propeller blades. By July 1915 the new forward-firing machine guns with their interrupter gear were flying on Fokker scouts. That advantage only lasted until the Allies adopted the idea, too.

The war's huge demands saw aircraft construction change from individual, hand-built jobs to mass production methods first developed by the growing auto industry. That industry also contributed to what was perhaps the greatest advance in aviation for that time—lightweight, more powerful gasoline engines that were dependable and durable.

The French and Germans in particular made rapid progress in this field. French aircraft were powered by excellent, mass produced Hispano-Suiza, Le Rhone, Gnome, Renault, and Clerget engines. Reliable Benz, Daimler and Mercedes engines powered German warplanes. Early British aircraft also used these engines until Rolls-Royce, Bentley Sunbeam and Beardmore engines were produced in quantity. In the final year of the war, the Americans came out with the remarkable 12-cylinder, 400 horsepower Liberty gasoline engine which powered the U.S.-built version of the deHavilland DH-4 bomber.

Harnessing the power of these engines were propellers with designs and structures far superior to the crude, paddle-shaped affairs of the prewar years. Rigid specifications, based

a—Curtiss scout plane (1913) fitted with nine-foot Paragon propeller with flywheel and chain-drive transmission typified U.S. military aircraft just prior to World War I.

b—Fabricating a wooden propeller was a painstaking process. Photographs below show major steps: marking a plank's center, gluing laminates together, roughly shaping the propeller by chisel and measuring and finishing the blades.

c—During the 1916 border war between U.S. and Mexico, wooden propellers on the U.S. Army Curtiss JN-4 trainers dried and split in 130-degree F. (55 C.) heat. Frank Caldwell, then a young Curtiss engineer, set up this makeshift shop in the New Mexican desert where 80 propellers of native wood were fabricated to replace them.

d—Shapes of propellers used during the war varied widely.

a

b

c

d

a

b

a—Sometimes all it took to complete balancing a propeller was a dab of paint or shellac on a blade's tip.

b—The giant Simmons propeller was typical of the propellers manufactured for World War I dirigibles.

c—Excellent workmanship of American Propeller's Paragon propeller for the Hispano-Suiza engine can be seen in the smooth fit of the long, curved metal sheaths used for erosion protection.

c

on the latest in aerodynamics, materials and fabrication techniques, were used to mass produce them. They not only detailed design procedures but specified the wood materials, their tensile strength and stress characteristics.

Much had been learned about lamination methods to fully utilize wood's inherent strength since the Wrights first carved the Flyer's propellers. A one piece, wood-blade propeller typically was built up by hand in blocks of five to 10 laminations that were planed, coated with hot hide glue, then compressed. The propeller blank was left to dry for 10 days or so to allow for adjustment of the glue stresses. The blades were shaped by hand. After inspection of its blade pitch and hub dimensions, the propeller was finished with several well-rubbed coats of spar varnish or hot-boiled linseed oil. Metal sheathing, usually copper, protected the blade tips.

The propellers were mass balanced to prevent their severely shaking the engine and aircraft. During the carving stage, a propeller's balance was frequently checked on knife edges to determine which side was heavier, and a small amount of wood was trimmed off that side. Final balance was accomplished usually by dabbing extra varnish on the lighter blade's tip.

Rudimentary as they may be by today's sophisticated standards, these propellers embodied the most advanced technology of the day, and the one with the outstanding reputation for thrust efficiency and durability continued to be the Chauviere Integrale. The beginning of the war, in fact, found British and German companies making the Integrale under license until they could build propellers of their own design.

Blade shapes and construction methods were many and varied. Some, like the Chauviere, had blade planforms with a curved leading edge and straight trailing edge. The Rapide (France) and Excelsior (U.S.) had curved trailing edges and straight leading edges. The blade of the Normale (France) was rectangular in shape while the Garude (German) blade was given a forward dihedral angle to alleviate bending stresses. Many designers attempted to synthesize the best of these features in their propellers with varying degrees of success.

There were a few flexible propellers, too. The Lavasseur (France) and Paragon (U.S.), for example, used blades with pronounced S-shaped planform that twisted the blade as thrust levels changed. On takeoff, blade pitch decreased enough to allow the engine to develop full running speed and power. When the aircraft reached altitude, the blade returned to its original, higher pitch to hold the engine at its normal cruise speed and power output. This built-in or "automatic" variable-pitch propeller, copied widely by other manufacturers, presaged some of the new developments that were to come in the post-war years.

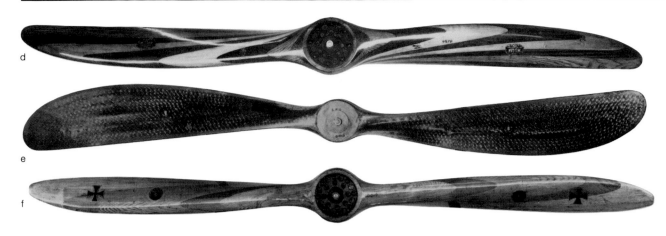

d—German Wotan propeller was made of laminated mahogany and ash. A 10-foot diameter Wotan was designed for the Benz 200 horsepower engine.

e—Riveted metal sheathing protected this English-built experimental Integrale wooden propeller against machine gun and antiaircraft fire.

f—The Germania propeller, fabricated from walnut and ash, had a 9½-foot diameter.

g—Eddie Rickenbacker with SPAD XIII, an outstanding French fighter.

h—Line-up of Royal Air Force Sopwith Camel fighters.

g

h

b

c

d

e

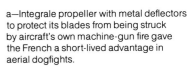

a—Integrale propeller with metal deflectors to protect its blades from being struck by aircraft's own machine-gun fire gave the French a short-lived advantage in aerial dogfights.

b—Sopwith Camel

c—DeHavilland DH1A fighter, early World War I

d—DeHavilland DH-4 bomber converted into a transport

e—French Nieuport 17 scout

f—Fokker D7 biplane fighter

g—English RAF FE2b bomber

h—English Handley Page 0/100 bomber

i—Curtiss Jennie, equipped with a Hamilton wooden propeller, served as a trainer for fledgling pilots in the U.S. Army Signal Corps.

a

f

g

h

i

j

k

j— Royal Aircraft Factory SE5A fighter

k—German Gotha II long-range bomber

5

VARIABLE PITCH AND METAL, TOO

*Dr. Sylvanus Albert Reed accidentally invents
the duraluminium blade. The ground adjustable propeller changes
blade pitch for better flight performance.*

With the signing of the Armistice, the thousands of people on both sides who built and flew warplanes, found themselves looking for other work. Former military pilots took to barnstorming, stunt flying and making intercontinental flights.

Converting their surplus aircraft, European countries underwrote commercial air transport and, by 1920, had a network of regular passenger service linking most major cities on the continent. In the United States, commercial aviation began with government-funded transcontinental airmail runs in 1920. Airline passenger service, however, didn't officially begin until April 4, 1927.

Toward the mid-1920s demands for new military aircraft and more comfortable, safer commercial transports stimulated aircraft production and advances in design and construction. Many technical advances were a carryover from the latter years of the war: metal aircraft, stressed skin structures, strong light metal alloys, fully cantilevered wings, enclosed cabins, supercharged engines and high-lift devices.

Not the least of these were the refinements made to enhance the propeller's performance and durability. This period saw two major breakthroughs: one-piece metal propellers and the ground adjustable propeller whose blades could be manually changed before a flight for optimum pitch setting.

The durability of wooden propellers was limited by their inability to withstand the effects of extreme variations in temperature and humidity on the glued joints and the impact of sand, stone, rain and sea spray. Attempts to protect the blades from erosion had proved short-lived. The typical service life of the wooden propeller generally lasted no more than six months.

There also was an aerodynamic problem. The propeller's higher blade velocities were approaching the speed of sound, but at these near-sonic speeds, the wooden propeller, with the thick aerofoils needed for stiffness, would suffer compressibility losses caused by the shock waves. The more durable blade material being sought also would have to allow for the construction of thinner blades to achieve propeller efficiency at the higher speeds.

In the search for better material, Micarta and Compreg were tried in the early 1920s. Micarta, developed in the United States, was made of fabric layers impregnated with a synthetic resin binder and baked under pressure. Compreg, a somewhat similar material invented in Germany, utilized hardwood laminates impregnated with phenol-formaldehyde resin and compressed at elevated temperatures into the propeller's final shape. Propellers in both materials turned out to be heavier and more expensive to make than in wood, and improvements in their ability to resist erosion and weathering were only marginal.

While metal was an obvious alternative, its greater density meant a weight penalty unless more efficient structures were

a

b

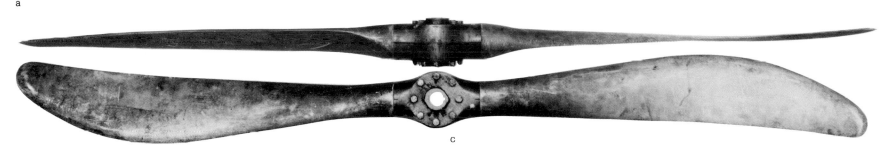

c

d

e

a—Hamilton Aero of Milwaukee was an outgrowth of Matthew Bros., one of scores of World War I propeller manufacturers.

b—Faehrmann's experimental steel propellers (Germany) featured steel plates riveted to steel ribs. Close-up shows unusual retention of the four ribs.

c—Dural-blade adjustable pitch propeller built by Inglis M. Uppercu in 1914 was the granddaddy of its type. Bolted split hub which allowed ground adjustment of blade pitch was widely used in the 1920s.

d—One-piece hollow steel propeller (1918) was designed by Thomas A. Dicks, left.

e—Production line of wooden propellers in the mid-1920s.

devised to allow the use of less material. True, some prewar pioneers had used steel and aluminium blades, but these were simple in design, with little if any aerodynamic and structural refinements.

At the outset metal propeller research conducted in England, France, Germany, Russia and America concentrated on steel because its strength characteristics and fabricating methods were well known. However, the early steel-blade propellers were less efficient than wooden ones, and none of the many experimental models progressed beyond flight test.

Other investigators turned to aluminium, specifically duralumin, an aluminium-copper alloy invented in Germany in 1903. Nearly as strong as mild steel, duralumin, or dural, still possessed the low density and lightweight properties of aluminium. In World War I, all-metal planes using dural were built by Junkers and Dornier. They also had tested rather crude dural propellers. An American, Inglis M. Uppercu, had experimented with an adjustable pitch propeller with dural blades as early as 1914, but the fatigue strength of the cast dural proved to be too low.

While others worked with dural as well, it was Dr. Sylvanus Albert Reed who discovered the modern dural propeller, and his discovery came by accident as is sometimes the case in technical breakthroughs. In studying high frequency acoustics, Reed, an engineer and inventor, used a revolving apparatus with thin dural blades to minimize driving-power requirements. One day he noticed that even though the device rotated at supersonic tip speeds, the arms were strong and rigid enough to withstand the aerodynamic forces.

Reed wondered if perhaps he had discovered a propeller that could operate with low drag at supersonic tip speeds. An extensive series of wind tunnel and flight tests proved him right. They confirmed that the performance of a thin-blade propeller did not experience any sharp degradation when blade velocities exceeded the speed of sound.

b

a

c

Reed's forged dural propeller was successfully flight tested on August 30, 1921 on a Curtiss Standard aircraft powered by an 160 horsepower engine. His success earned him instant fame in the aviation world and the Collier Trophy, the top aviation award in the U.S. His propellers, widely used by air racers of the day, were manufactured under license by such companies as Curtiss in the U.S., Fairey in England and Lavasseur in France, in addition to his own company.

Wooden and one-piece metal propellers shared a common limitation—fixed blade pitch or angle. For a specific aircraft installation, the blade's pitch had to be set for maximum performance at either takeoff, cruise or some compromise in be-

d

e

a—Dr. Sylvanus A. Reed stands next to his forged dural propeller for which he won the 1925 Collier Trophy.

b—These Junkers propellers illustrate why damaged aluminium blades could be readily repaired and wooden ones could not.

c—This Reed dural propeller was made in England by the Fairey Aviation Company, Ltd., a licensee.

d—Jimmy Doolittle won the 1925 Schneider Trophy Race in this Curtiss R3C-2 seaplane fitted with a thin-blade Reed propeller.

e—With a U.S. Navy crew of five, Lieutenant Commander Albert C. Read flew the Curtiss NC-4 flying boat on the first transatlantic flight in 1919. One of three aircraft, it flew from Newfoundland to England, via the Azores.

f—President Calvin Coolidge welcomes U.S. Army crew members who flew Douglas World Cruisers around the world in 1924. Two of the four DWCs finished the 26,345-mile voyage in 175 days.

f

tween, and that pitch was shaped into the blades at the time of fabrication.

What was needed was the ability to adjust blade pitch quickly and accurately in the field, without removing the propeller from the engine. Young Geoffrey deHavilland invented a ground adjustable propeller in 1908 but used the pitch-change feature merely to determine the best setting for flight testing his first experimental aircraft.

Uppercu's 1914 metal propeller also was ground adjustable, with cast-dural blades clamped in a split bronze hub. Different blade retention methods were tried by other ground-adjustable experimenters. However, they were structurally inadequate for the high, steady centrifugal and vibratory forces exerted on them.

Within the decade, with their added knowledge of blade aerodynamics, centrifugal loads and material strengths, engineers like Frank Caldwell and Thomas Dicks were able to solve the problem. They developed steel hubs and better retention techniques to hold the forged aluminum, hollow steel and wooden blades of the ground adjustable propellers that were widely used during the late 1920s and early 1930s.

The best propeller of the time was the dural-blade ground adjustable propeller, and most of the record-blazing pilots like Clarence Chamberlain, Frank Hawks, Wiley Post and General Italo Balbo had their planes fitted with them.

Another exceptional pilot was Charles A. Lindbergh. In preparing for his solo transatlantic flight, he carefully supervised every aspect of the Spirit of St. Louis's design and fabrication. For the propeller, he chose a dural-blade ground adjustable made by the Standard Steel Propeller Co., one of the ancestors of Hamilton Standard.

Lindbergh and Standard's engineers considered whether the blade pitch should be set to favor cruise conditions to conserve fuel consumption in flight or takeoff conditions to lift the heavy fuel load. After some deliberation, they chose a cruise setting but with the blade angle at ½ degree below optimum as a concession to the power needed for take-off. That concession, small as it was, probably made a big difference—the Spirit of St. Louis cleared the telephone wires at the end of Roosevelt Field by a mere 20 feet.

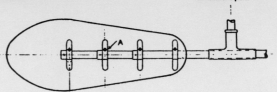

a

b

b

c

a—Advantage of adjustable pitch propellers was discussed by English engineer Geoffrey deHavilland in this 1910 letter to *Flight* magazine. Sir Geoffrey founded the deHavilland Airplane Company in 1920.

b—Famous propeller-driven racers in the early 1930s included the Granville Gee Bee, top, and Wedell-Williams Racer.

c—Douglas designed its Mailplane to meet the all-weather rigors encountered by regular airmail service.

d

e

f

d—Hall Racer featured a gull wing.

e—Starting an engine of a Royal Aircraft Factory Sopwith SE5 as spectators, probably at a Farnborough Air Show, look on.

f—Chance Vought came out with the first of a proud line of Corsair fighters in the late 1920s. This one used a Standard Steel ground adjustable propeller.

g—Aviation leaders pose with Charles A. Lindbergh, second from right, and his record-setting Ryan monoplane. They are, from left: B. F. Mahoney, owner of Ryan; Harry Guggenheim, head of a foundation which strongly supported aviation; and Charles L. Lawrence, president of Wright Aeronautical Corporation, which supplied the engine.

g

6

THE COMING OF AGE

*The ability to vary blade pitch in flight gives pilots
a much-needed aerial gearshift. Aerodynamicists learn more about
the impact of vibrations and propeller behavior.*

Lindbergh's solo, New York-to-Paris flight on May 20, 1927 rekindled public enthusiasm for aviation. A young airline industry, enjoying wider acceptance, looked for aircraft that could fly faster, farther and with more passengers. More efficient, more durable propellers were needed to replace the ground adjustable type which, because of its pre-set blade angle, either restricted cruising speed or imposed poor takeoff performance.

Engineers turned to the variable pitch propeller that would allow the pilot to change blade angle in flight, giving him high thrust needed for takeoff and climb (low pitch) and peak cruise and high altitude performance (high pitch). The idea of varying the blade angle is as old as the propeller itself. Early innovators, even with their little knowledge of aerodynamics, were aware that changing blade pitch changed the propeller's thrust output. Finding the mechanical means of doing it, however, proved too formidable a task for the technology at hand, and only a few concepts were tried, with little success.

A French patent for a variable pitch propeller dates back to the 1700s, although whether one was ever built is unknown. In 1909 Chauviere used mechanical linkage with which the pilot could twist the blades of its one-piece propellers to change their pitch. Paragon and Lavasseur made wooden propellers (c. 1913) with thin, flexible blades that automatically twisted under changing air loads.

Of these and many others, the most successful was a con-trollable and reversible pitch propeller developed and flight tested in the U.S. by Eustis and Hart in 1917. This propeller had wooden blades set in a steel hub and mechanically actuated by cables from the cockpit. However, the blade retention experienced too much friction at high tip speeds.

What especially attracted engineers now were the tremendous performance advantages promised by the variable pitch propeller. Compared to fixed pitch, their predictions showed, the ability to change blade angle in flight offered aircraft up to 40% more thrust at takeoff and an up to 60% faster rate of climb.

In 1922 a mechanically actuated, two-position variable pitch propeller with better blade retention was patented by Frank Caldwell, then chief of propellers with the U.S. Army Signal Corps. Seven years later he patented a hydromechanical version which, successfully flight tested in 1932, was first used on the Douglas DC-2 transport. His development of this "gear shift of the air" won Caldwell the 1933 Collier Trophy.

The Europeans, meanwhile, also were working on variable-pitch methods. In England, the Hele-Shaw-Beacham propeller, hydromechanically actuated, was invented in the mid-1920s. The Gloster Aircraft Company, undertaking its development in 1926, extensively flight tested the propeller on Grebe and Gamecock single-engine fighters. In 1925 Junkers in Germany flight tested a two-position controllable propeller electrically actuated by magnets, but it never proved com-

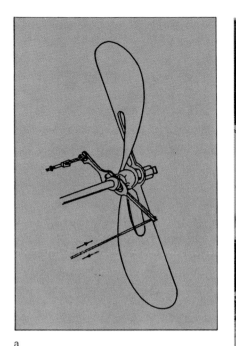

a

c

b

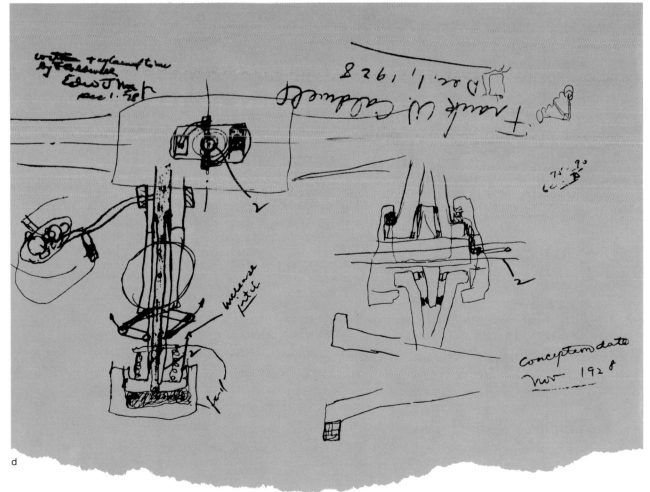

d

a—Chauviere's concept of a variable pitch propeller (c. 1909) used this mechanical arrangement to manually twist the wooden blades.

b—Cables by which pilots changed the propeller's blade pitch in flight were tested on a Royal Aircraft Establishment SE5 biplane.

c—First manually controllable and reversible propeller made by Standard Steel (c. 1920) had hollow steel blades.

d—Frank Caldwell illustrated his hydro-mechanical pitch-change design for a 1928 patent application.

a

b

a—President Franklin D. Roosevelt presents Frank Caldwell with the 1933 Collier Trophy for developing a practical variable pitch propeller.

b—England's Hele-Shaw-Beacham variable pitch propeller was patented before Caldwell's but moved slower into production. It later became the basis for the Rotol propeller.

pletely practical. Ratier in France developed a pneumatically actuated propeller, but it was limited to one pitch-change in flight and only saw service on a few sport and racing aircraft.

A variable pitch propeller actuated by electric motor was successfully flight tested by Wallace R. Turnbull in Canada in 1927 and by Vickers in England the following year. In the U.S., Thomas Dicks at Standard Steel worked on a mechanically actuated, controllable and reversible propeller similar to the Eustis and Hart design. Its one innovation was an experimental hollow steel blade which Dicks developed when he later formed his own company.

This prolific period of aviation advances also saw the emergence of the world's premier manufacturers of large-diameter propellers. In the U.S., United Aircraft Corporation, predecessor of United Technologies Corporation, formed the Hamilton Standard Propeller Company in 1929 by acquiring Hamilton Aero and Standard Steel. Curtiss Aeroplane Company set up a propeller division two years later and broadened its capabilities by purchasing the rights to the Turnbull electrically actuated propeller, Reed dural blade propeller and Dicks hollow steel blade.

In England, the deHavilland Aircraft Company, manufacturer of commercial and military aircraft since World War I, also got into the propeller business in 1934 when it signed an agreement to produce Hamilton Standard's controllable pitch propeller. The association was prompted by deHavilland's entry in the MacRobertson England-to-Australia Race later that year. The company's sleek, twin-engine D.H. 88 Comet Racer incorporated the latest aeronautical features such as wing flaps and retractable undercarriage, and Geoffrey deHavilland and his team of engineers decided that it was essential to have the most advanced propeller, too.

Since there were no manufacturers of variable pitch propellers in the United Kingdom at the time, deHavilland engineers visited Ratier and Hamilton Standard. While its propeller—already in production—demonstrated the reliability and efficiency they were looking for, Hamilton Standard couldn't design and deliver it in time for the race. Instead, the Englishmen chose the Ratier variable pitch type which, although less sophisticated, was available.

The Comet won the race in the elapsed time of 71 hours. (Interestingly enough, the contestants that came in second and

c

d

c—Commemorative painting shows the grinding of the first deHavilland dural blade as Geoffrey deHavilland and Charles Walker, chief engineer, look on.

d—One of the most daring long distance flights was made by Sir Charles Kingsford-Smith, an Australian, in his rebuilt Fokker Trimotor Southern Cross. In 1928 he and a crew of four flew from Oakland, California, to Brisbane, Australia.

third, a KLM Royal Dutch Airlines Douglas DC-2 and a Boeing 247D, both transports, were equipped with Hamilton Standard controllables.) DeHavilland had already decided to get into the variable pitch propeller business and picked the Hamilton Standard propeller because of its more advanced design and the good service record it was experiencing on American-built commercial transports. DeHavilland organized a propeller division the same year the agreement was signed, then established the deHavilland Propeller Company in 1946 as a separate company at Hatfield.

Hamilton Standard, because of the popularity of its controllable pitch propeller, also signed manufacturing agreements with companies in eight other countries during the mid-1930s. These included Hispano-Suiza in France, Junkers in Germany, Fiat in Italy and Sumitomo in Japan which already was making Hamilton Standard ground adjustable propellers under an earlier license.

Rolls-Royce and Bristol Aeroplane Company jointly organized Rotol Airscrews Ltd. in England in 1937 to develop a line of controllable pitch propellers based on the Hele-Shaw-Beacham hydromechanical design. The company was purchased by the Dowty Group in 1960 to form today's Dowty Rotol Ltd. Ratier, which began producing fixed pitch, wooden

propellers in 1906, became the dominant French propeller company, first manufacturing electrical, then hydromechanical propellers. Junkers, an airplane and engine maker like the English and U.S. companies, became the biggest propeller producer in Germany. VDM Company was another prominent German propeller maker.

Significant improvements in propeller performance rapidly followed one after the other during the rest of the 1930s. The constant speed control gave pilots what, in automotive terms, essentially was an automatic shift. It used a governor which, once the pilot set the engine rpm, maintained that speed while blade pitch automatically changed, according to climb, cruise and other flight regimes. The constant speed was a great improvement over the variable pitch propeller's two-position manual control. With this refinement, the blades could assume any position between high and low pitch.

Following three years of development, Hamilton Standard came out with its Hydromatic propeller in 1938. Its double-acting hydraulics changed blade pitch faster over a wider range than its predecessors. The Hydromatic also introduced a new blade control function: feathering. Feathering, used when a power plant malfunctioned, added considerably to the flight safety of multiengine aircraft. Changing blade pitch to a 90-de-

a

a—In its time the German flying boat Dornier DO-X was the largest aircraft ever built. On its inaugural flight in October 1929, it carried 169 passengers. It used 12 propellers, six pusher and six tractor, or puller, types.

b—Lockheed Electra 10A transport.

c—The deHavilland Comet Racer won the London-to-Melbourne race in 1934. It was equipped with Ratier controllable pitch propellers actuated pneumatically.

d—Navy Grumman SF-1 scout

e—Sikorsky S-42 Clipper Ship.

f—Shorts Empire flying boat

b

c

d

e

f

a—This Bristol 142 transport was fitted with deHavilland controllable pitch propellers. In 1935 "Britain First" 142 ordered by Lord Rothemere, the English press baron, reached a speed of 307 mph, 50 to 100 mph faster than any current RAF fighters. The Blenheim bomber was based on the 142's design.

b—Ford Trimotor transports, originally equipped with ground adjustable propellers, were refitted with controllable pitch propellers.

c—Amelia Earhart is cheered after completing her 1935 solo flight from Honolulu to Oakland in a Lockheed Vega.

a

b

c

d—DeHavilland's Albatross and Flamingo transports both used its constant speed propellers.

e—Hamilton Standard Hydromatic propeller on Douglas DC-3 transport is shown feathered and in low pitch.

f—Development of the constant speed propeller was spurred by the potential take-off and climb benefits it provided over two-position control.

d

d

e

gree angle (toward the aircraft's line of flight) stopped the propeller's rotation, or windmilling, which previously could do more damage to a malfunctioning engine and could even tear it from the aircraft. Feathering a dead engine's propeller also lessened drag which gave the pilot more control of the aircraft.

Knowledge of the propeller's aerodynamic and structural behavior also grew during this period. Techniques for measuring blade vibration stresses in flight were pioneered by Charles Kearns at Hamilton Standard, Norman Hadwin at deHavilland and Ralph Guerke at Curtiss. These tests led to refined analytical methods used to design metal blades that could withstand the higher vibratory loads placed on propellers by increasing engine power and airspeeds.

Application of the vortex theory, or strip analysis, gave propeller engineers a precise tool for analyzing the aerodynamic distribution of loads on blades for the first time. This analytical work, headed by George Rosen at Hamilton and Hank Borst at Curtiss, was based on the earlier works of C.N.H. Locke of the Royal Aircraft Establishment who systematized the vortex theory first promulgated by Prandtl and Glauert in Germany a generation earlier. Through extensive blade and hub testing, more also was learned about the physical properties of dural and steel, the propeller's primary materials, to provide designers with better fatigue data.

f

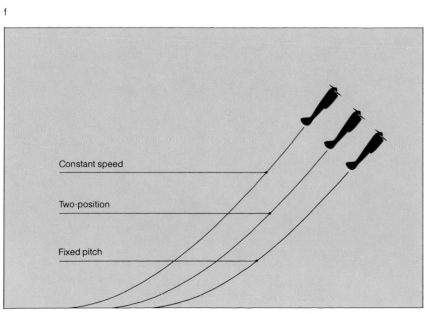

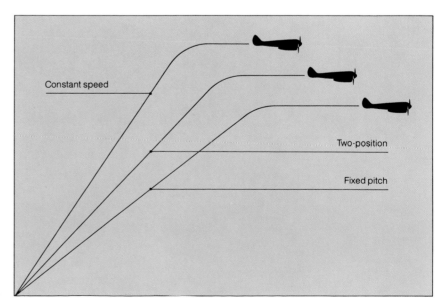

a—First public demonstration of a feathered Hamilton Standard Hydromatic propeller was made by a United Air Lines DC-3 over New York City on April 6, 1938.

b—This drawing shows how a feathered propeller allowed a plane to fly at twice the ceiling level of a braked propeller.

c—French Moraine-Saulnier fighter had a cannon that fired through a hollow propeller shaft.

d—Unique, one-blade Everel (U.S.) propeller used a simple method to automatically vary blade pitch. Maintaining a balance between centrifugal and aerodynamic forces, it changed blade pitch according to engine speed. The Everel proved practical only on very small, low powered aircraft.

e—This Ratier counter-rotating propeller, 11 feet in diameter, was used on the French VB10 fighter powered by two, tandem-mounted Hispano-Suiza 1350 horsepower engines.

a

b

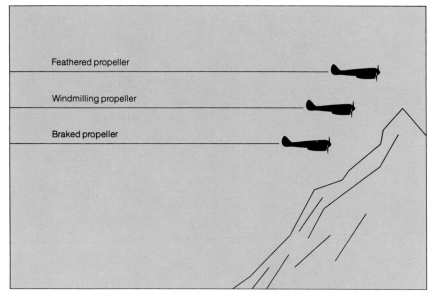

Feathered propeller

Windmilling propeller

Braked propeller

c

d

e

f—Handley Page Hampden, top, and Bristol Blenheim, pre-World War II bombers, had deHavilland constant speed propellers.

g—Curtiss controllable-pitch propeller, with reversible and feathering features, used an electric motor for pitch actuation.

g

The propeller, specifically the constant speed propeller, played a vital role in the Battle of Britain and the Royal Air Force's halting the Luftwaffe's attempt to soften up England for Hitler's planned invasion from continental Europe. Even though deHavilland's agreement with Hamilton had been extended in 1937 to include the manufacture of constant speed propellers, the British Air Ministry initially allocated these propellers to multiengine aircraft, primarily heavy bombers.

During the air battles over France in 1940, the RAF fighters, equipped with two-position, variable-pitch propellers, were being outmaneuvered and outclimbed by German aircraft. With the prospect of facing the Luftwaffe alone for control of the skies over Great Britain, the RAF undertook a crash program to convert all Hurricanes and Spitfires to constant speed propellers so they could climb faster and higher to intercept the German fighters.

DeHavilland received verbal instructions to begin the conversion on June 22, 1940. While deHavilland accelerated production of constant speed propellers, Hamilton Standard rushed conversion kits and some key people to help RAF and deHavilland crews install the first round of constant speed propellers. At the conversion's peak, deHavilland and RAF teams worked an average of 110 hours a week—sometimes putting in as many as 20 hours a day. In some squadrons as many as four or five Spitfires were converted and test flown in one day. Arduous as the work was the project had its lighter moments. In one instance, a deHavilland contracts employee—worried about the lack of a government contract, impossible delivery dates and some highly irregular goings-on, cautioned: "We shall never get paid for this." Whereupon an engineer replied: "And if it isn't done, we may never live to be paid for anything."

By August 16, nearly two months after the Herculean effort began, exactly 1,050 Spitfires and Hurricanes were converted—an average of 20 a day. In the crucial days between August 8 and 16 some of these RAF fighters shot down 80 Luftwaffe aircraft. Only 20 RAF fighters were lost. The scales of the air battle had tipped, and, as one high ranking officer in the Fighter Command remarked, "But for the conversion job, the figures might have been reversed."

The dural blade proved to be remarkably durable in combat. Even though the propeller's blade suffered the most damage, techniques were developed to file away the rough edges and straighten the bent blades without any appreciable weakening of the dural's structural strength. Bases in England repaired nearly 25,000 blades, some of them more than once.

Thanks to the propeller's ability to feather, many combat-damaged aircraft—particularly bombers which sometimes had two, even three damaged engines shut down—were able to return to their bases safely. Significant, too, were the methods used to overhaul pitch-change mechanisms. Many of the makeshift procedures that evolved at the maintenance depots served as models for the worldwide networks of field service stations established to support commercial aviation after the war.

a

a—Bristol Beaufort torpedo bombers. More than 2,000 were built, 700 of them in Australia.

b

c

d

e

b—Vickers Wellington, the RAF's main
bomber early in the war.

c—Avro Lancaster bomber

d—Boeing B-17 Flying Fortress

e—North American P-51 Mustang

a

b

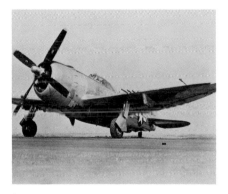

c

d

e

a—U.S. Navy Vought F4U Corsair

b—Boeing B-29 Super Fortress heavy bomber

c—North American B-25 Mitchell

d—U.S. Navy Grumman TBF torpedo bomber

e—Republic P-47 Thunderbolt

f—The "Swoose Goose" (half swan, half goose), a B-17 built from cannibalized parts of wrecked bombers, toured the U.S. on several War Bond drives.

f

a

b

a—Luftwaffe Heinkel He-111 bomber

b—Messerschmitt Bf-109s

c—British Coastal Command's Sunderland,
left, and Shorts Shetland flying boats

d—Focke-Wulf Fw-190

c

d

e

f

e—Mitsubishi Zero was the Japanese Navy's highly maneuverable fighter.

f—Douglas A-26 attack aircraft

g—Consolidated B-24 Liberator bomber

g

Although everyone's energies focused on meeting prodigious production demands, the propeller did make some major technological strides during the wartime. Blade cuffs and conically shaped spinners were added, primarily to fighter propellers, to further reduce drag and increase engine cooling. Experimental work continued on the reversible pitch propeller, hollow steel blades, chemical deicing, blade synchronization and other refinements for the coming boom in the production of commercial transports.

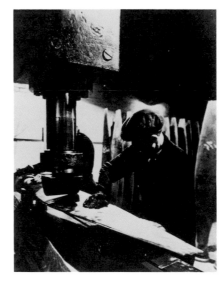

a

a—Bent blades are repaired by cold-straightening methods.

b—War-damaged dural propellers wait for repair at deHavilland.

c—Damaged dural blades at Hamilton Standard's East Hartford facility.

b

c

d

e

f

d—A contra-rotating propeller is flight tested on a Spitfire.

e—Repaired propeller undergoes stress tests at deHavilland.

f—Hamilton Standard tested propeller improvements during the war in this East Hartford test house.

g—Contra-rotating propeller with six blades was developed by deHavilland.

g

8

MEETING CIVILIAN PENT-UP NEEDS

The propeller becomes king of the commercial airways.
The need for higher thrusts leads to the development of lightweight
blades using fiberglass-reinforced composites.

With one ear tuned to the whine of the emerging gas turbine engine, the propeller makers turned their attention to commercial aviation's pent-up need for yet another round of high-speed, high-altitude transports. Responses to this demand initially came from the United States and United Kingdom, the only nations whose ability to build aircraft had survived the war.

In 1946 Hamilton Standard, for instance, put its combat-proven Hydromatic propeller into civilian production. The United Air Lines Douglas DC-6 airliner was among its first users. Three years later this propeller, with either solid dural or new hollow steel blades, became standard equipment on the majority of new commercial transports.

Based on the earlier Hydromatic, the improved model featured reversible pitch, automatic synchronization and electrical blade deicing. Moving the blade angle to a negative pitch not only reversed the direction of propeller thrust but stepped it up to takeoff levels. The reverse thrust, combined with wheel brakes, often halved the distance of an aircraft's landing roll.

Synchronizing the rotation of propeller blades eliminated the annoying "beat" experienced when propellers on multi-engine aircraft turned at slightly different rotational speeds. The electrical synchronizer, sensing such variations, automatically adjusted individual governors until all propellers ran at the same speed.

Eliminating propeller beat and sound proofing the cabin made airline travel a more comfortable experience. Automatic synchronizing also relieved the crew from manually fine tuning engine speed in flight. The electrical deicers replaced the less effective practice of melting ice on propeller blades by spraying (by centrifugal force) the blades with a chemical, usually glycol.

Equally important were the engineering refinements that greatly enhanced the reliability and performance of the hydro-mechanical pitch-change mechanism. The new Hydromatic used its own oil supply instead of the engine's for actuation purposes. This eliminated sludge and metal chips in the engine's oil from clogging the control's passages, thus hampering the responsiveness of propeller-pitch changes which sometimes had resulted in engine overspeed.

Hamilton Standard developed a "compensated" governor that changed blade pitch extremely fast—from 30 degrees to 50 degrees a second. This system controlled engine speed more accurately, and the rapidity of its blade pitch-change enabled the propeller to effectively produce the reverse thrust the bigger transports needed immediately after touchdown.

In the United States, the new generation of propeller-driven transports started with the Douglas DC-4 and Lockheed Constellation, which were quickly followed by the DC-6, Lockheed Super Constellation, the Boeing Stratocruiser, then the DC-7. In the U.K., propellers were being produced for piston-engine civilian transports like the Avro Tudor, Handley Page Hermes, Bristol Freighter, Vickers Viking, Percival Prince, Airspeed Ambassador and deHavilland Dove.

a

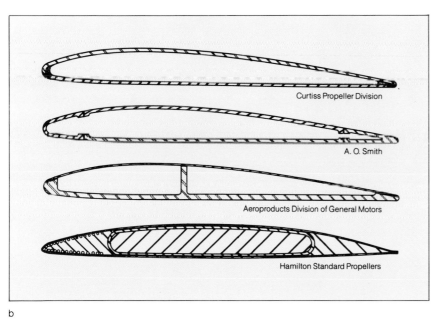

b

c

d

e

Curtiss Propeller Division

A. O. Smith

Aeroproducts Division of General Motors

Hamilton Standard Propellers

a—To produce the post-war era's higher thrusts, the propeller blade's chord was widened more and its tip squared off.

b—Four concepts of hollow steel blades manufactured in the U.S.

c—Spar for hollow steel blade undergoes cold rolling.

d—Steel spar hot-formed at Hamilton Standard.

e—Hot forming spars at deHavilland.

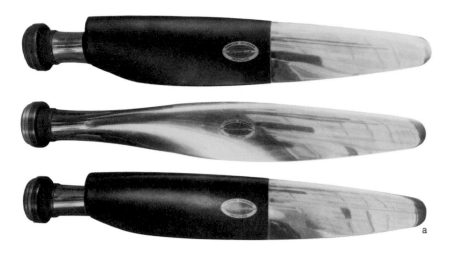

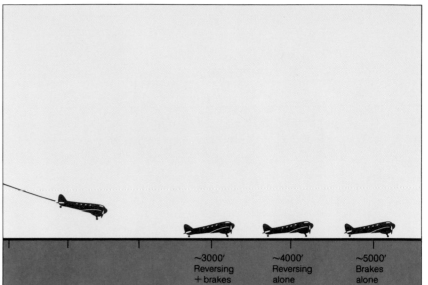

a—Molded rubber cuffs at the blade roots provided more cooling for high-powered piston engines.

b—Landing with reversible propellers

c—Hamilton Standard propeller spinners

d

d—Electrical deicers on a deHavilland propeller tested on a Hastings aircraft.

e—Douglas DC-4 commercial transport

f—Cold-room facilities like this one were used by propeller makers to test hydro-mechanical components under simulated high-altitude and Arctic conditions.

g—DeHavilland used this Hatfield test cell for propeller aerodynamic and engine tests.

e

f

g

In meeting this period's propulsion needs, including the supercharged engines developed for high-altitude flying, designers were faced with an increasingly critical problem—how to handle the greatly increased power without the propeller's blade tips touching the runway. Propeller diameters before the war had approached 13 feet, adequate for the relatively low-powered engines (1000 hp) and low-speed aircraft (150–200 mph at cruise) of the day. More powerful engines and much faster aircraft of the post-war period, however, also meant wider blades which threatened to add too much weight to the propeller.

Applying refined strip analysis methods, aerodynamicists designed rectangular blades that equaled the efficiency of the widely used tapered blade but more ably absorbed the much higher engine horsepower. Making the blade tip wider greatly improved the blade's thrust-to-weight ratio, allowing the propeller to better handle engines up to 3500 horsepower with only small increases in diameter and blade number. The wider tips also reduced the blade's thickness-to-width ratio to cope with the compressibility losses that otherwise would occur at the higher aircraft speeds.

a

The wider blades, nevertheless, didn't completely solve the weight problem of large, solid dural blade propellers. Like other experimenters before them, propeller designers turned to hollow steel designs. Curtiss and Aeroproducts used hollow steel blades but, because of their heavy wall thicknesses, they were not much lighter than comparably sized dural blades.

Following up on work done under U.S. Navy auspices during World War II, Hamilton Standard chose a blade that used a hollow steel spar to carry the main structural loads and covered it with a thin-walled steel shell, aerodynamically shaped to form the blade. The spar and shell were brazed together, and the blade's inside cavities were filled with a low-density foam to keep the thin outer shell from "tin canning."

To produce these two-piece blades, Hamilton Standard developed some innovative tooling. Tube reducers were used to cold-roll steel tubes with tapered outside diameters and wall thicknesses. Vertical furnaces on moveable tracks heated the spars and shells to 1700 degrees Fahrenheit (930 degrees Centigrade) while high temperature vertical presses die-formed spars and shells which were internally pressurized with an inert gas to prevent the steel from oxidizing. The shell and spar were joined in brazing furnaces.

DeHavilland Propellers put this hollow steel blade in production in England. While adopting most of the same fabricating techniques as Hamilton Standard, the company used horizontal rather than vertical presses to shape the spars and shells and machined the steel spars instead of using tube reduction methods.

The hollow steel propellers (flight tested in 1945) made by both companies drove a variety of commercial and military aircraft. DeHavilland versions were fitted on the Bristol Britannia airliner and Blackburn Beverley military transport.

b

c

a—Boeing Stratocruiser

b—DeHavilland Heron medium-range airliner

c—Airspeed Ambassador short-range transport.

d—DeHavilland Dove, another short-range transport

d

e

f

g

e—Lockheed Constellation

f—Martin 404

g—Convair 340

h—Vickers Viking medium-range transport

h

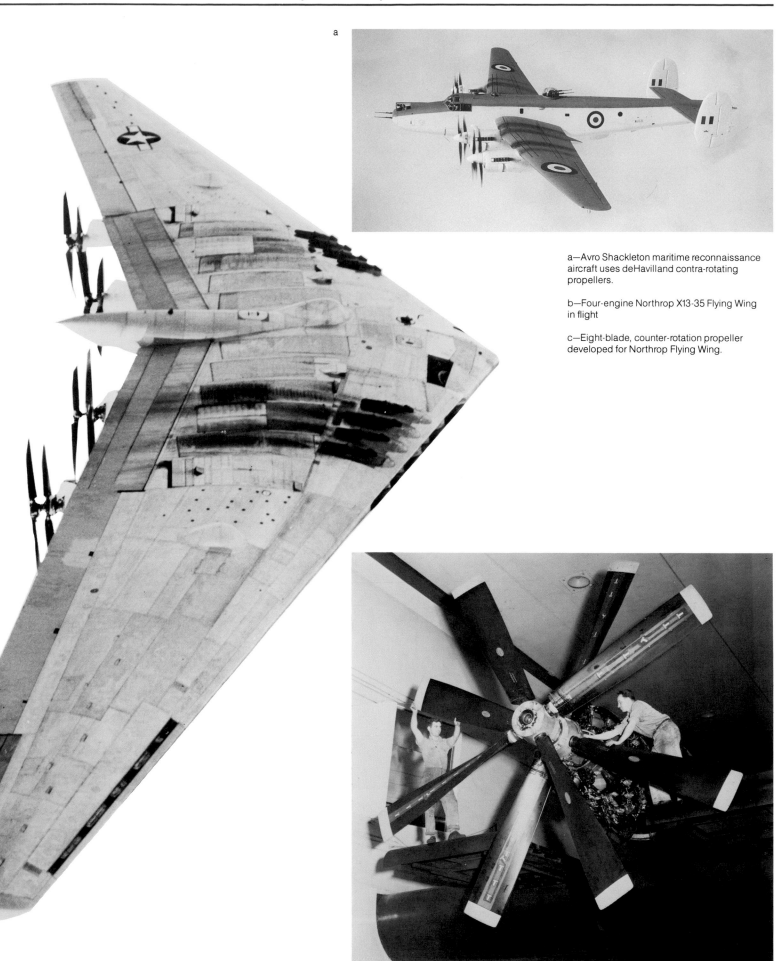

a

a—Avro Shackleton maritime reconnaissance aircraft uses deHavilland contra-rotating propellers.

b—Four-engine Northrop X13-35 Flying Wing in flight

c—Eight-blade, counter-rotation propeller developed for Northrop Flying Wing.

b

c

d

d—The Lockheed P2V submarine-patrol aircraft initially used Hamilton Standard propellers with hollow steel blades. It was later used to test the company's fiberglass shell/steel spar blades (1967).

e—DeHavilland of Canada Otter at the South Pole

e

9

THE PROPELLER TURNS TURBINE

The jet engine's popularity relegates the propeller
to the lower spectrum of subsonic speeds. V/STOL and hovercraft requirements
advance propeller technology for future applications.

The immediate post-war years saw the tried and true propeller and the new gas turbine merge into the turbine propeller (turboprop) power plant. In addition to turning the pure jet's compressor, the gas turbine was given added stages to generate the added power needed to drive the propeller. Reduction gearing linked the propeller to the turbine's drive shaft. The British who, like the Germans, had actually put the gas turbine in production near the war's end, introduced the world's first turboprop airliner in 1948—the Vickers Viscount powered by four Rolls-Royce Dart engines and Rotol dural-blade propellers. The first generation of turboprop transports soon included the Bristol Britannia, Fokker F-27 Friendship, Avro 748 and Handley Page Herald.

Operating typically at up to 2500 shaft horsepower, these propellers incorporated sophisticated controls and pitch-change mechanisms for safety purposes because the gas turbine was more sensitive to rpm changes than the reciprocating engine. Even more complex were the turboprops developed for the second generation transports, military as well as civil. They absorbed more than twice the shaft horsepower of their predecessors. The majority of the new transports were equipped with deHavilland propellers which had four wide-chord, aluminum alloy blades. The propellers on the Vickers Vanguard, Canadian CL44 civil transports, and the Transall C160 military aircraft ranged from 14½ to 18 feet in diameter. Hamilton Standard, which had flight tested its TurboHydromatic in 1950, developed large-diameter propellers for the Lockheed C-130

military transport and Lockheed P3V, a submarine hunter. General Motors, in addition to supplying engines for these aircraft, produced Aeroproducts propellers for the Lockheed Electra, civilian version of the P3V first put into service by Eastern Airlines in 1959.

At medium subsonic speeds, the turbine-driven propeller proved to be more efficient than the turbojet because less energy was lost in its slower slipstream. At high subsonic speeds, however, propeller designers ran into their recurring problem —compressibility losses caused by shock waves that degraded the blade's lift-to-drag ratio and thus its performance. Propeller-driven aircraft, therefore, only could achieve speeds of Mach 0.6 (400 to 450 mph) while turbojet-powered airliners could cruise at Mach 0.8 (500 to 600 mph).

Compressibility losses, wind-tunnel testing showed, could be mitigated by very thin blades with swept-back or other dramatic shapes. The high-speed propeller's need for wide, superthin blades of hollow construction also was prophetically put forth in 1954 by Guy Gardener and Jack Mullin, deHavilland's chief engineer and chief aerodynamicist respectively, in an article published by the Journal of the Royal Aeronautical Society. However, the aerodynamics and blade structure technology were not in hand at the time to put such radically shaped blades in production. The turbine propeller was relegated to tasks at more moderate speed ranges. In time it became widely used on private and executive transports (the general-aviation type) and certain specialized, multiengine military aircraft.

a

b

c

a—DeHavilland supplied turbine propellers for the Vickers Vanguard.

b—Some Viscounts were fitted with deHavilland dural blade turbine propellers.

c—The world's first turbine propeller transport to enter airline service was the Vickers Viscount equipped with Rotol propellers.

a—DeHavilland experimental high-speed propeller blade

b—Hamilton Standard test high-speed blades

c—George Rosen inspects propeller model with high-speed blades.

d—The Saunders-Roe Princess flying boat was powered by 10 engines driving deHavilland propellers.

e—The Bristol Britannia used deHavilland propellers.

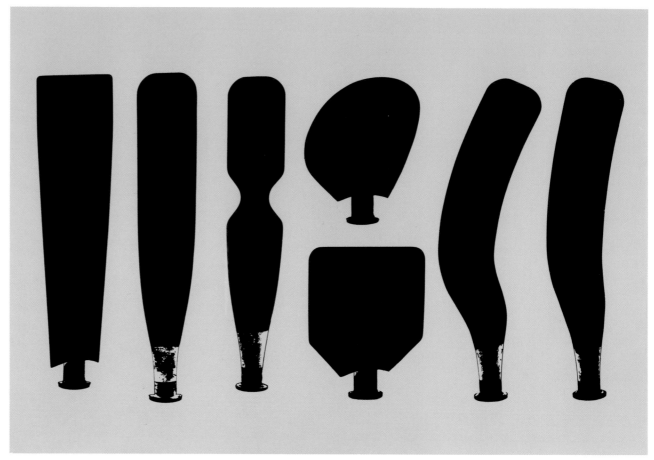

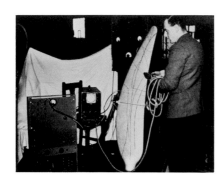

a

b

d

c

e

f

g

h

f—French-built Breguet Atlantic, with
deHavilland turbine propellers

g—Fokker F-27 Friendship short-range
turboprop

h—Transall C160 short-range transport

i—Russian Tupolev Tu-104 transport

i

hovercraft and other vehicles designed to skim over land and sea on a cushion of air.

Most of these projects involved propellers. Two American V/STOL programs were the Ling-Temco-Vought XC-142, a box-car shaped transport with four large propellers mounted on a tilting wing, and the Bell X-22, which had tandem wings with two tilting, shrouded propellers on each. In Canada, the Canadair CL-84 VTOL featured a tilt-wing with two propellers on it. The VC-400 being developed by Vereinigte Flugtechnische Werke (VFW) of West Germany had tandem wings, with two large tilting propellers on each. At the same time England, France and the U.S. also worked on hovercraft-type vehicles designed to operate in coastal waterways.

These projects placed extremely tough demands on propeller technology. For taking off from a standing start, the V/STOL-type propeller had to produce much higher thrusts than ever before. The propulsion package, along with the airframe itself, had to weigh substantially less. And its control had to be refined so that the propeller could react very quickly when the aircraft was hovering or making a transition from one flight mode to another.

Most important of these requirements was trimming the propeller blade's weight. Hamilton Standard's ambitious development program had brought forth a producible fiberglass shell/steel spar blade that was structurally sound and weighed half as much as a comparably sized solid dural blade. The fiberglass shell had been found to be susceptible to erosion, but that problem was solved by placing nickel sheathing along the blade's leading edge. Hamilton Standard first put the new composite blade into production in the mid-1960s for propellers that replaced the hollow steel versions on the Navy P2V submarine-patrol aircraft.

It was during this same period that Hamilton Standard applied the fiberglass shell/steel spar blade to the propellers it developed for the XC-142 and X-22A V/STOL airplanes. For the Canadair CL-84's propellers, Curtiss developed monocoque fiberglass blades whose outer skin carried the stresses.

England's deHavilland Propellers, which had become Hawker Siddeley Dynamics in 1963, developed a line of large solid dural and later composite blade propellers for hovercraft. The largest of these amphibious craft shuttle across the English Channel between the U.K. and France, their propellers producing both forward thrust and directional control. Smaller hovercraft, many fitted with Dowty Rotol propellers, ply coastal waters.

Although they had the same shell/spar design as Hamilton, deHavilland's propellers used an aluminum alloy spar bonded to the glass-fiber reinforced aerodynamic shell. The largest, such as the four propellers on the British Hovercraft Corporation's SRN-4 Mk3 Mountbatten, were 21 feet in diameter. This line of propellers were protected from sand and sea erosion by nickel or titanium applied on the blade leading edges. It also was designed to operate at tolerably lower noise

a

b

a—DeHavilland of Canada Buffalo STOL aircraft with Hamilton Standard turbine propellers

b—Turbine propellers being manufactured at deHavilland's Hatfield factory.

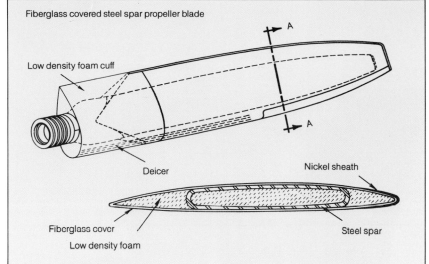

Fiberglass covered steel spar propeller blade

Low density foam cuff

Deicer

Nickel sheath

Fiberglass cover

Low density foam

Steel spar

d

c

c—Dural blade is balanced vertically.

d—Cross-section of Hamilton Standard fiberglass shell/steel spar blade.

e—Early fabrication of glass-fiber reinforced blades at Hamilton Standard.

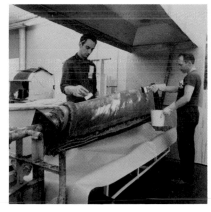

e

b

a

a—The SRN-4 Mountbatten hovercraft

b—Composite blade with dural spar is
manufactured for the 21-foot diameter
propeller used on the SRN-4 hovercraft.

c—This U.S. hydroskimmer used Hamilton
Standard propellers with dural blades.

c

d

d—The French-built Sedan N500 hovercraft also was fitted with deHavilland fiberglass blade/dural spar propellers.

e—The SRN-6 hovercraft uses Dowty Rotol composite or solid dural blade propellers.

e

10

MOVING IN NEW DIRECTIONS

Its inherent fuel and thrust efficiencies firmly place the propeller on commuter transports. For larger airliners of the 1990s, the radically new Prop-Fan promises to cut fuel use substantially yet match jet speeds.

The acute fuel shortage that followed the 1973 Arab oil embargo triggered profound and permanent changes in aviation. Until then airlines had been spending about 20% of their operating costs for fuel. Four years later the sharp escalation of prices had driven that figure to nearly 50%. Suddenly, the fuel consumption characteristics of aircraft propulsion became a primary concern of those who built, powered and flew aircraft.

To make aircraft (particularly commercial transports) more fuel efficient, new technologies were applied in high-temperature materials, combustion processes, turbofan engines with higher bypass ratios and airframe aerodynamics. In the U.S., the National Aeronautics and Space Administration began a long-range Aircraft Energy Efficiency Program, funding advances in technologies of the turbofan and turboprop engines that would power aircraft in the 1990s.

The Airline Deregulation Act passed by Congress in 1978 brought partial relief to the U.S. airlines. It allowed them to withdraw from unprofitable routes which were mainly those serving the smaller cities in their networks. This in turn opened the short-haul routes to the regional, or commuter, airlines, accelerating their growth and stimulating their demand for new fuel-efficient transports capable of carrying from 10 to 80 passengers. Also, large international corporations, many of them with decentralized operations, had a growing need for short-range aircraft to transport key personnel and critical materials between their widely spread facilities.

Demand for more commuter and executive aircraft and more fuel-thrifty power plants sparked the rejuvenation of the propeller industry which had experienced lean times through the 1960s. Based on their V/STOL and hovercraft work, the propeller makers applied advanced technologies to a new family of propellers.

The performance of these commuter propellers is superior to earlier turboprops in a number of ways. They are quieter not only to reduce cabin noise but to comply with low-noise standards set for communities neighboring the small airports used by commuter transports. While approximately the same size in diameter, the new propellers produce higher thrusts over a wide range of operating conditions.

Furthermore, their composite blades make them up to 50% lighter than turbine propellers with solid dural blades. Many commuter propellers feature blade angle control which the pilot uses to override the constant speed control and directly change blade pitch, providing faster thrust response during taxiing and landing. Modular in design and with many fewer parts, the commuter models in most cases can be maintained without removing them from the aircraft.

Hamilton Standard's first commuter propeller flew on the deHavilland Dash 7 four-engine, 50-passenger transport in 1975. To cut noise, it runs at two-thirds the tip speed of previously developed propellers. To get more thrust out of such

Fully assembled commuter propeller

a—Hubs of Hamilton Standard commuter propellers are produced by computer-aided manufacturing techniques.

b—Completed composite blades are carted to Hamilton Standard assembly floor.

c—Injection-molding process produces matched, interchangeable dural spar/fiberglass shell blades.

a

b

c

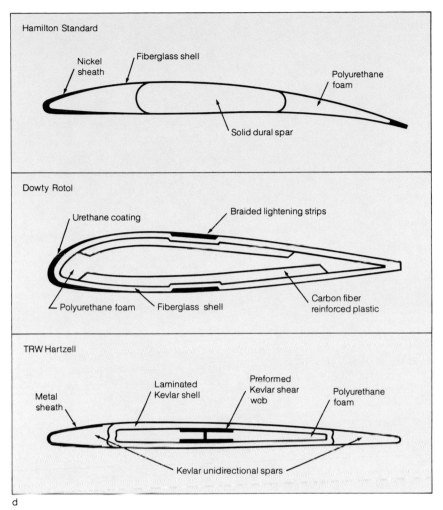

Hamilton Standard

Nickel sheath · Fiberglass shell · Polyurethane foam · Solid dural spar

Dowty Rotol

Urethane coating · Braided lightening strips · Polyurethane foam · Fiberglass shell · Carbon fiber reinforced plastic

TRW Hartzell

Metal sheath · Laminated Kevlar shell · Preformed Kevlar shear web · Polyurethane foam · Kevlar unidirectional spars

d

e

low rpms, designers widened the four blades. The blades have a load-carrying solid dural spar, foam core and fiberglass shell. The composite blades make the propeller so much lighter than the comparably sized (11¼ feet in diameter) solid dural blade turboprop that deHavilland was able to add four more passenger seats.

The two other leading suppliers of commuter propellers, Dowty Rotol and TRW Hartzell Propeller Company, also build their blades out of composites. Dowty Rotol uses the same design originally developed for its hovercraft propeller blades: a carbon spar, hard-foam core with a glass-fiber reinforced resin envelope. TRW Hartzell, the leading maker of general-aviation propellers in the U.S., has a composite blade with a Kevlar-fiber foam-core monocoque structure.

f

d—Lightweight composite blade designs

e—Canadian deHavilland Dash 7, 50-passenger transport was the first to use Hamilton Standard commuter propellers in 1975.

f—Shorts 360 is fitted with TRW Hartzell commuter propellers.

a

b

c

a—DeHavilland of Canada's 30-passenger Dash 8 . . .

b—Embraer Brasilia . . .

c—Aerospatiale ATR-42 commuter transports, all equipped with Hamilton Standard propellers.

d

e

f

d—CASA-Nurtanio CN235

e—Template layouts of dural spar forgings for ATP's composite blades are checked before machining.

f—Model of British Aerospace ATP transport's six-blade propeller is prepared for test.

In tailoring the propeller to commuter-aircraft requirements (less noise and weight, more efficient thrust), engineers had to replace the blade airfoils they had commonly used for many years with a new set with higher load-carrying and higher lift/drag ratio characteristics. Dowty Rotol, assisted by the Aircraft Research Association, designed new aerofoil sections for general-aviation and commuter propellers in 1974. Hamilton Standard also developed a new family of high-cambered (curvature) airfoils partially based on the experimental work of Richard T. Whitcomb at NASA's Langley Research Center. These airfoil families have allowed designers to build quiet-operating lightweight propellers with narrow blades that can produce thrusts equal to those of wide blades on earlier turboprops.

However, there is a practical limit to how much camber can be put on these new airfoils without losing their lift-to-drag advantage. To handle growing engine powers without increasing noise or propeller diameter and blade width, more blades are being added to the commuter turboprop which until recently has generally had four blades.

The British and Americans had experimented with five-blade propellers during World War II. On a commercial basis, Hartzell became the first to supply five-blade propellers; they are used on the Shorts 330. A six-blade propeller is being jointly developed by Hamilton Standard and British Aerospace's Dynamics Group for the new British Aerospace ATP (Advanced Turboprop), a twin-engine 64-passenger commuter transport. The new Fokker F-50 commuter is equipped with a Dowty Rotol six-blade propeller.

In attempts to build faster, more fuel-efficient transports, some airframe designers have revived the canard-type aircraft reminiscent of the Wright brothers' forward-wing and pusher propeller configuration. Mounting the turboprop behind the wing smooths the air flowing over the wing, boosting flight speed by 50 mph to 60 mph. Noise and vibrations in the cabin are also reduced, although designers must contend with the vibratory stresses on the blades that are exacerbated by the turbulent wing wake. The Beech Starship 1, LearFan 2100 and Gates Learjet/Piaggio GP-180 executive aircraft feature pusher propellers.

For larger and faster fuel-efficient airlines of the 1990s and beyond, Hamilton Standard is developing the Prop-Fan. Innovative in design and very promising in performance it is undoubtedly the most advanced turboprop propulsion system the aviation industry has seen in decades. In 1974 Hamilton Stan-

a—Fokker 50 commuter transport with six-blade Dowty Rotol propellers.

b—Saab/Fairchild 340 also uses Dowty Rotol turboprops.

a

SE-ISF

b

c

c—Artist's concept of British Aerospace ATP commuter transport

d—Full-scale ATP propeller is prepared for engine test.

d

a—Early Prop-Fan model undergoes wind
tunnel tests.

b—Canard-type Beech Starship 1

a

b

c

c—Flight test of Prop-Fan model's acoustic characteristics are conducted by NASA.

d—Hamilton Standard used British-built Fairey Gannet to conduct Prop-Fan-related acoustic flight tests.

d

a

b

c

a—Model of Gulfstream II modified for
full-scale Prop-Fan flight test.

b—Concept of counter-rotation Prop-Fan

c—Full-scale Prop-Fan mockup

d—Aircraft concept shows
rear-mounted, counter-rotation Prop-Fans.

d

dard studied the feasibility of this new concept, an outgrowth of its advanced work. Based on the study's design and performance findings, NASA the following year began supporting Hamilton's development of the Prop-Fan as part of its long-range aircraft energy efficiency program. The agency also has funded extensive design studies conducted by airframe and engine manufacturers.

The reason for this ongoing interest is the Prop-Fan's impressive performance projections—up to 25% savings in fuel while matching the speed and comfort of the commercial jets air travelers are accustomed to riding. For 150-passenger transports flying at Mach 0.8 speed, a Prop-Fan typically would be up to 14 feet in diameter in size and be driven by engines of about 15,000 horsepower. The eight to 10 composite blades, its most unusual feature, are thin yet very wide, closely spaced and swept back at an angle of 35 to 40 degrees.

Having completed wind tunnel tests on subscale models, Hamilton Standard is constructing a full-scale Prop-Fan nine feet in diameter with eight composite blades. The NASA-funded program involves component testing, wind tunnel tests of the assembled Prop-Fan which then will be flight demonstrated in 1987 on a Gulfstream II jetliner converted into a flying test bed.

Looking to improve performance even more, meanwhile, Hamilton Standard has conducted studies indicating that twin, counter-rotation Prop-Fans could cut fuel consumption by an additional 10%. Supporting flight tests of counter-rotation propellers also showed that most of the moderate increase in cabin noise fell within the high frequency spectrum which can be attenuated by sound-absorbing materials.

In the Prop-Fan's development, Hamilton Standard is using the latest design techniques. Designers are applying the lifting-surface theory to create more accurate aerodynamic and acoustic modelling of the more complex Prop-Fan blade. This advanced design tool predicts precisely the aerodynamic loads across the blade's chord, or width. Developed originally by Prandtl for wing design in 1936, the lifting-surface theory supplements the lifting-line vortex theory which considered blade loads acting along a single longitudinal line but couldn't predict the aerodynamic behavior of wide, swept-back blades.

Today the aircraft propeller once again stands at another technological threshold. From obscure origins to the only means of propelling aircraft to the turboprop, it has played a leading and vital role in the progress of aviation. It has faced the threat of near-extinction. Thanks to its inherent efficiencies and the vision of the managers of the few companies that advanced them, the propeller did more than simply survive. It has carved a new, growing niche in the commuter-aircraft field, and the Prop-Fan's development promises to greatly expand its application among the larger, faster transports of tomorrow.

The story of the propeller doesn't end here. It continues.